The Story of Science
in America

The Story of Science in America

by L. SPRAGUE DE CAMP
and CATHERINE C. DE CAMP
illustrated by Leonard Everett Fisher

CHARLES SCRIBNER'S SONS   NEW YORK

Text Copyright © 1967 L. Sprague de Camp
Illustrations Copyright © 1967 Leonard Everett Fisher

A–9.67[V]

Printed in the United States of America
Library of Congress Catalog Card Number 67-23686

CONTENTS

PART ONE
Science Comes to America

I · SCIENCE IN THE COLONIES

Today, the United States of America leads the nations of the world in science. This was not always so. Before the American Revolution, the thirteen English colonies in the New World were scientifically backward.

In George Washington's day, there were no professional scientists, although a few men, mostly physicians, dabbled in such sciences as botany and astronomy in their spare time. Although the American colonists were more literate than many peoples of that time, most of them were not much interested in scientific developments. For some, the way that their parents had done things was good enough for them. Sitting and thinking they considered a waste of time; finding the facts of nature they deemed irreligious; and people who undertook scientific research they looked upon with scorn and suspicion.

This state of affairs continued long after the United States had become an independent nation and pioneers had worked their way westward over the Appalachian Mountains. Not until the later nineteenth century did any large number of Americans begin to regard pure science as useful, worthy, and important.

Most early Americans were unscientific as a result of the hard, isolated lives they led. Nearly all of them were farmers. Their few cities were actually small towns, loosely connected by narrow dirt roads. Life, by modern standards, was rough, difficult, and dirty. Although people had enormous families, many of the children died of disease before they grew up. There was no system of government aid for the poor. Parents had to be resourceful and endlessly busy, building their own houses, growing their own food, making their own clothing, and educating their own children. They had little time for studying the nature of the world around them.

Although there were a few small colleges and universities in colonial cities, these taught mostly law, religion, and ancient languages. Scientific courses were few, and those that existed did not teach a great deal. Even at the grade-school level, there were no free public schools. Since only a few private, church, and charitable schools existed, many people grew up without any schooling at all.

Moreover, the first, small-scale attempts of the American colonists to make inventions and develop industries were stifled by the governors sent from England. In the seventeenth and eighteenth centuries, the leading nations of Europe set up their colonies solely for the benefit of the mother nation. For example, the British government expected the Americans to send raw materials and farm produce to Britain and to buy manufactured goods in return. To make sure that the colonists played their part in this economic plan, Britain passed laws forbidding Americans to make such things as steel, felt hats, and woolen goods. American resentment against these laws helped to bring about the American Revolution.

Because our forefathers worked so hard to make a living, because so few had schooling, and because their mother country discouraged invention, the people of colonial America knew little about science in spite of the scientific and industrial revolution then taking place in Europe.

Science is the process of adding to man's knowledge of nature in an intelligent and orderly way. It is the deliberate discovery of facts not known before and of laws that explain these facts. The ancient Babylonians and Egyptians were the first to record the facts of nature. The Greeks of the centuries before Christ and the Arabs of the Middle Ages carried scientific discovery further.

In the sixteenth and seventeenth centuries, a host of European scientists—men like Nikolaus Copernicus (1473–1543), Johannes Kepler (1571–1630), Galileo Galilei (1564–1642), and Sir Isaac Newton (1642–1727)—made so many important discoveries that man's ideas about the universe were greatly changed. This flowering of scientific research took place, at first, mainly in England, France, and Italy. Later Germany, the Low Countries, and Scandinavia also produced a number of great scientists.

Scientific ideas are like the pollens of flowers: they waft from nation to nation and are quickly put to use. The early great discoveries of science, little by little, even traveled across the ocean to America, where they at last stimulated Americans to make their own discoveries and, in time, to catch up with and pass the rest of the world in science. This book will tell you about the awakening of scientific interest in America, about the outstanding American scientists, and about the marvelous civilization that they have done so much to build in the last three centuries.

In 1662, two men conferred in London. One was John Winthrop the Younger (1606–76), governor of Connecticut. He was a long-nosed, scholarly man of fifty-six who owned one of the largest libraries in the colonies.

The other was Robert Boyle (1627–91), a tall, gaunt man of thirty-five who looked too frail to support the enormous wig that fashion compelled him to wear. Boyle, who lived at Oxford in a house cluttered with scientific apparatus, was already famous for writing the first modern definition of a chemical element and for inventing an air pump. He had discovered that air, when compressed in a cylinder, acted as a spring; as the pressure on the piston increased, the volume shrank in inverse proportion—that is, when one was doubled the other was halved.

Boyle had come to London to attend a meeting of a new society: the Royal Society of London for Improving Natural Knowledge—or, as it was coming to be known, simply the Royal Society. Such scientific societies were being founded in many European countries to speed the progress of science by enabling scientists to keep in touch with each other's work.

Seventeenth-century Britain saw an outburst of scientific genius. Robert Boyle the chemist, Isaac Newton the mathematician, Robert Hooke (1635–1703) the physicist, Edmund Halley (1656–1742) the astronomer, Christopher Wren (1632–1723) the astronomer and architect, John Locke (1632–1704) the philosopher and psychologist, and William Dampier (1652–1715) the naturalist—who was also a practicing pirate—all lived and worked in England or Scotland during these splendid years.

Winthrop had taken the long journey to England, partly to ask Boyle how to encourage scientific research in America. As yet, there had been no attempt at research of any sort in the colonies, except for the occasional work of visiting scientists like Thomas Harriot (1560–1621). Harriot had sailed to Virginia with Sir Walter Raleigh in 1585 and later published an accurate report about the plants and animals of that new land. He described for his English readers such strange and fascinating creatures as the skunk and the opossum.

Winthrop listened to Boyle's advice and returned to Connecticut with a telescope three and a half feet long. For nine years, when not otherwise occupied with the cares of the office, he spent his nights peering at the heavenly bodies. Once he thought that he had found a fifth moon of Jupiter to add to the four that Galileo had discovered. Winthrop was mistaken: the fifth moon was there, of course, but it could not be seen with a telescope so small as his.

By 1672, Governor Winthrop found all-night star-gazing too hard on his health and gave his telescope to Harvard College. At Harvard, the telescope was used by Thomas Brattle (1657–1713), a Boston-born merchant who had become the richest man in New England and who, at the same time, was proud to be another pioneer in American science.

Brattle, an amateur mathematician and astronomer, made a long series of observations with the Winthrop telescope. He sent his data back across the ocean to the Royal Society, and his studies of a comet visible in 1680 were passed on to Edmund Halley and Isaac Newton. Newton included this information in his great *Philosophiae Naturalis Principia Mathematica* (*Mathematical Principles of Natural Philosophy*), published a few years later. This work, one of the most important scientific books of all time, set forth Newton's discoveries in physics, mechanics, and astronomy and laid down the laws by which the heavenly bodies move.

In later years, Brattle quarreled with one of the most influential men in Boston: the Reverend Cotton Mather (1663–1728), a Congregationalist minister, scientist, and writer. Cotton Mather, a stout, pop-eyed man, was intelligent and able, but also vain, quarrelsome, excitable, moody, and a fanatical believer in witches.

For more than two hundred years, Europeans had lived in desperate fear of witches. They believed that certain men and women worshiped the Devil and thus gained the power to cast harmful magical spells on their neighbors. During the worst period of the witch panic in Europe, more than half a million people were cruelly killed as witches.

By 1692, the terror of witchcraft had died down in Europe. But an outbreak of the madness struck Salem Village in the Massachusetts Bay Colony that year and led to the hanging of nineteen accused witches and the execution of another by piling weights on him. Cotton Mather attended all the trials and urged on the prosecution. Therefore, unfortunately, most people remember him as a witch hunter rather than as a scientist.

Yet, as a scientist, Cotton Mather was perhaps the leading man of his day in the Americas. He wrote a total of 450 books and articles, one of which introduced science to the general public. Although this book, *The Christian Philosopher,* published in London in 1721, is not easy reading by modern standards, it is the forerunner of today's great mass of popular-science writing.

In the chapter entitled *"Of the* VEGETABLES," Mather made his main contributions to science. He endorsed the theory—which had been developed 2,000 years earlier by the Greek botanist Theophrastos but which had long been forgotten—that plants have sex. He also announced three discoveries of his own. He observed that some plants are fertilized when the wind blows pollen from one to the other. He found that plants of two different species can sometimes be crossed to produce a hybrid. He saw that, in plants as well as in animals, offspring sometimes resemble one parent the more and sometimes the other. He wrote:

My Neighbour planted a Row of Hills in his Field with our *Indian Corn,* the rest of the Field he planted with Corn of the most usual colour, which is *yellow.* To the most *Windward-side* this Row infected *four* of the next neighbouring Rows, and part of the fifth, and some of the sixth, to render them colour'd like what grew on itself. But on the *Leeward-side* no less than seven of the eight Rows were so colour'd, and some smaller impression made on those that were yet further distant. . . .[1]

Mather went on to tell how the same neighbor planted gourds in his garden among the squashes in the hope that any thief who might try to steal his squashes would carry off the gourds instead and find his prize inedible. Unfortunately, the squashes crossed with the gourds and produced a plant no more edible than a gourd and far less useful.

In the same year that *The Christian Philosopher* appeared, smallpox struck Boston. At that time, a crude form of inoculation was practiced in Asia and Africa. Two European physicians learned how inoculations were given in Turkey and sent accounts of the procedure to the Royal Society. The Royal Society printed these articles in its *Philosophical Transactions,* the leading scientific journal of its day.

Cotton Mather had already heard about inoculations from a slave given him by his grateful parishioners. After he read the articles in the *Transactions,* Mather summarized the procedures and sent copies of his summary to all the physicians in Boston. He also wrote to Dr. Zabdiel Boylston (1679–1766), urging him to try out this new method of conquering the deadly disease of smallpox.

The first inoculation against smallpox was given in 1721. Starting with his own family, Boylston inoculated many Bostonians. Some people denounced the unfamiliar practice as unsafe and ungodly, much as certain people have recently denounced the fluoridation of drinking water as a Communist plot. One of them threw a bomb into Mather's study, complete with sputtering fuse and a note that read:

Cotton Mather, you Dog; Dam you: I'l enoculate you with this, with a pox to you.[2]

The bomb failed to go off, although a guest of the family, who was sleeping in that room, was frightened out of his wits.

Mather and Boylston persisted until they were able to state in a pamphlet that of 241 patients inoculated in one month, only six died, and of these, at least four had already been infected at the time of inoculation. This pamphlet was one of the first attempts to use statistics to decide the efficacy of a new medical procedure. As a result of Mather's concern and his scientific studies, inoculation for smallpox was widely accepted in America. True, the early method was crude and not entirely safe; but it was much safer than the disease it combated.

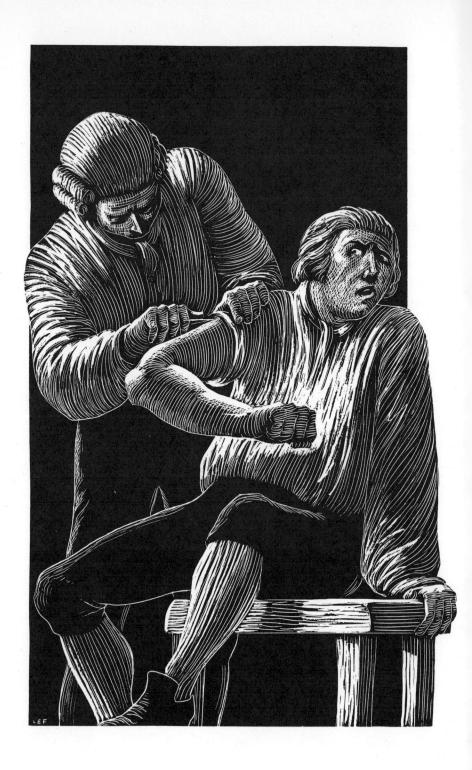

In 1724, a large, muscular youth visited Mather to ask his advice. The young man was Benjamin Franklin (1706–90), a native of Boston who worked for his brother as a printer's apprentice until, after many quarrels, he ran away to Philadelphia.

Cotton Mather loved to give advice to young people. He showed Franklin into his study, where the motto BE SHORT! hung over the door. After a lengthy chat, the old preacher showed his visitor out by a back hall. When Franklin hit his head on a low crossbeam, Mather gave him a final wise piece of advice: "You are young, and have the world before you; stoop as you go through it, and you will miss many hard bumps." [3]

II · BENJAMIN FRANKLIN'S CENTURY

The outstanding American of his time was Benjamin Franklin, beloved by people of every degree on both sides of the Atlantic. This versatile genius was not only a cultivated man of the world, who served his country as Ambassador to France during the American Revolution, but also a distinguished journalist, a successful businessman, and an active civic leader. He organized a municipal fire department, developed city street lighting, and urged adult education for the citizens of his adopted city of Philadelphia. Despite his many other activities, Franklin also pursued a scientific career so active that his discoveries dominate eighteenth-century American science.

Franklin had no formal education in science, because such a thing as a scientific education was unknown in the thirteen American colonies. Some of the best scientific training of the time—such as it was—was furnished by the universities of Edinburgh, in Scotland, and Leyden, in the Netherlands; but Franklin started life as a poor boy from a large family who, by the time he was fourteen, had to support himself as a printer's apprentice.

Nevertheless, his scientific bent showed itself early. As a youth in Boston, he invented paddles to be held in a swimmer's hands to increase his speed. As a young adult, Franklin was busy making a good living as a printer, writer, publisher, and politician. Yet he found time not only to set up a discussion group called the Junto but also to wonder about the absorption of heat by materials of different colors. He decided to lay squares of colored cloth on a snowbank in the sun. In a few hours,

. . . the black, being warmed most by the sun, was sunk so low as to be below the stroke of the sun's rays; the dark blue was almost as low, the lighter blue not quite so much as the dark, the other colours less as they were lighter; and the quite white remained on the surface of the snow, not having entered it at all.[1]

In 1742, Franklin made his first important invention: a much-needed stove. The open fire, glowing cheerfully in colonial homes, let four-fifths of the heat escape up the chimney. Although the open fire served adequately in Europe, such fires failed to keep the house warm in New England and Pennsylvania, where the winters are much more severe. While stoves of the German type were sometimes used in Franklin's Philadephia, they heated the same air over and over, until people could hardly breathe for lack of oxygen.

Franklin designed a larger hearth reaching well into the room, placed his stove upon it, and attached to the stove a long pipe, which carried the fumes up the chimney. This Franklin stove became the ancestor of all the kitchen stoves in the world. The governor of the colony offered Franklin a patent. But Franklin generously declined because: ". . . as we enjoy great advantage from the inventions of others, we should be glad of an opportunity to serve others by any invention of ours."[2]

However, Franklin did not object when, years later, the Constitution of the United States was so written as to allow the grant of patents to inventors. He knew that, as a successful businessman, he could afford to give his stove to the public, whereas most inventors needed the protection of patent laws.

As he neared forty, Franklin devoted more time to science. He founded the American Philosophical Society. This was a more formal and learned society than the Junto, which merged with the newer group.

At this time, Franklin was a heavy-set man with strong, square hands, a high-domed forehead, and long, light hair. His expressive eyes surmounted a big jaw and a wide, thin-lipped mouth. Although he was rather quiet and reserved in crowds, among his friends he was a delightfully witty conversationalist.

The leading botanist of the new society was a self-taught farmer who lived near Philadelphia. John Bartram (1699–1777) was the first native-born American naturalist. Fascinated by plants, he educated himself by poring over books borrowed from his neighbors—for in those days books were scarce in the colonies. Later, he found that he could make long trips around the country to gather plant materials each fall after his crops were harvested.

Botany was a popular hobby in Europe, especially in England. One amateur British botanist, Peter Collinson (1694–1768), a Quaker merchant, offered Bartram five guineas a box for American plants and persuaded some of his rich friends to do likewise.

Every fall, therefore, Bartram set off with a pack on his back, wandering all over the colonies. He went afoot, because he found that leaping off a horse every time he saw an interesting plant was more trouble than carrying his own pack.

One of Bartram's many botanical discoveries was the mountain bay or franklinia, a small tree of the tea family with huge pale-green leaves. The wild specimens collected by John Bartram and his son William were, strangely enough, the last of their kind. The plant has never been found in the wild state since their day. Although it is now grown as an ornamental tree, all specimens living today are descended from those that the Bartrams found, planted in their garden, and named in honor of Benjamin Franklin.

John Bartram corresponded not only with titled customers in England, but also with the Queen of Sweden and even with the great Swedish botanist Carolus Linnaeus, or Carl von Linné (1707–78). Linnaeus worked out a method of classifying all the living things in the world. He chose, as his smallest group, similar creatures that interbred freely. These he called a *species*. A group of similar species he named a *genus;* a group of genera, an *order;* a group of orders, a *class*. The largest groups that he recognized were the animal and vegetable kingdoms, each made up of a number of classes. This system of classification, with many later additions and refinements, is still in use.

In 1795, at the urging of Franklin and Collinson, King George III appointed Bartram the King's Botanist and promised to pay him fifty pounds a year. Alas! the King usually forgot to pay, and there was no way for Bartram to dun a king.

After John Bartram died, his son William (1739–1823) continued his work. William Bartram's lively accounts of travels in Georgia and Florida became popular reading in Europe. They influenced European writers, such as Samuel Taylor Coleridge, who borrowed from Bartram some of the scenery for his famous poem *Kubla Khan*.

In 1746, Franklin made a business trip to Boston. While there, he stopped to look at the exhibition of a Dr. Spencer, who had come from Scotland to demonstrate the wonders of electricity. Spencer's sparks and shocks did not work very well, because the damp air of Massachusetts allowed his electric charges to leak away. Nevertheless, Franklin became so interested that he bought the apparatus.

In late colonial times, electricity and magnetism were not entirely mysterious. The first serious research into both these forces was done by the physician of Queen Elizabeth I, William Gilbert (1540–1603). Gilbert not only discovered many of the laws of the magnet but also made the first clear distinction between magnetism and electricity. A short time later, the marvelous mayor of Magdeburg, Otto von Guericke (1602–86), invented an air pump, successfully predicted the return of certain comets, and constructed the first electrostatic machine. This was a big ball of sulfur turned by a crank. By brushing cloth or fingers against the spinning ball, an experimenter could generate static electricity, just as you do when you scuff your shoes on a deep-pile carpet on a cold winter's day.

The electric bottle, or Leyden jar, in which static electricity could be stored, was invented later. By means of the Leyden jar, a much stronger spark could be generated than with the electrostatic machine alone. The men who experimented with these devices in those days were called "electricians." The Abbé Jean A. Nollet (1700–70), "electrician" to King Louis XV, amused his master by making seven hundred monks hold hands. When the monks at the ends of the line touched the terminals of a charged electric bottle, the whole seven hundred got a shock and leaped, as one monk, into the air.

Largely unaware of the work of these earlier investigators, Franklin spent more and more time on his electrical experiments. He even persuaded some of his fellow members of the American Philosophical Society to join him in his research.

Franklin invented, or at least was the first to use in English, such terms as armature, brush, to charge and discharge, to conduct, to electrify, conductor, electric battery, electrical shock, electrician, plus or positive and minus or negative electricity, and many other now standard electrical terms. Besides performing stunts like those of Dr. Spencer, Franklin made three important discoveries about electricity. He found that a charge of static electricity tends to leak off charged objects at sharp points (the "point effect"); that electricity consists of one single "fluid," not two as some students had thought; and that lightning is a form of electricity.

Franklin discovered the point effect by a simple experiment. He hung a cork from his ceiling by a silken thread. When he pushed a charged metal ball toward the cork, the latter swung away, repelled by the electric charge. But, when he also thrust a needle close to the ball, the cork gradually swung toward the ball. The sharper the needle, the swifter the approach of the cork to the ball. Franklin quickly saw that the charge leaked off the charged body into the surrounding air at sharp points.

Franklin next attacked the two-fluid theory of electricity. He made his subjects stand on blocks of wax, to insulate them from the ground. Then, by rubbing a glass tube hanging from the ceiling, they charged both themselves and the tube with static electricity and exchanged charges by touching each other. By trying different combinations of charged and uncharged subjects, Franklin showed that the one-fluid theory would account for everything that happened. In other words, Franklin conceived that electric sparks were caused by an excess or a lack of the same "electric fluid," which was normally diffused all through matter.

Franklin made one mistake. He thought that, when he rubbed a glass tube, the "fluid" went into the glass. He therefore called the charge on the glass a "positive" charge. The evidence, however, indicates that electrons flow *out* of the glass when it is rubbed.

As a result of Franklin's belief, diagrams of electrical apparatus are still marked + at "positive" poles (in Franklin's sense) and — at "negative" ones, with arrows showing the current flowing from plus to minus. All scientists, however, speak of the stream of electrons as flowing from the "negative" to the "positive."

Franklin also noted that lightning and electric sparks were alike in shape, in color, and in swiftness. To prove that lightning was just a big electric spark (or, to put it another way, that an electric spark was merely a small flash of lightning) he proposed in a letter to mount "on top of some high tower or steeple . . . a kind of sentry box . . . big enough to contain a man and an electrical stand"; [3] that is, a sheet of in-

THE EXPERIMENT WITH LIGHTNING SUGGESTED BY FRANKLIN
AND PERFORMED BY D'ALIBARD (1752).

sulating material for the experimenter to stand on. A pointed iron rod was to be mounted on the insulator, bending its way out the door and projecting upward 20 or 30 feet. When a thundercloud approached, the rod would become electrified. Franklin believed that the experimenter could electrify himself by touching the rod, or he could produce sparks by moving a grounded wire close to the rod, so that electric current would flow between the rod and the ground.

A French scientist, Thomas F. d'Alibard, heard of Franklin's suggested experiment. He tried it out on May 10, 1752, and reported that it worked, just as Franklin had predicted.

Meanwhile, Franklin had thought up another proof that lightning was merely a big electric spark. About a month after d'Alibard's experiment, Franklin made a kite, using a large silken handkerchief and two sticks. One stormy day, he flew his little kite, with the help of his 21-year-old son William. Sheltered from the rain by a shed, Franklin watched the rising kite and presently saw the fibers of the kite string stiffen like the hair on the tail of a frightened cat. Placing his knuckle near a key tied to the string, he drew a spark and so completed his proof. Franklin was luckier than he realized. A little later, a Swedish professor in Russia, Georg W. Richmann (1711–53), was killed while repeating Franklin's experiment; for lightning is a dangerously powerful spark indeed.

Following his electrical experiments, Franklin conceived the idea of the lightning rod. When a thundercloud passes overhead, it bears either a positive or a negative charge. The earth beneath it becomes charged with an electric charge opposite to that of the cloud. If the charge is great enough, or the cloud hangs low enough, a spark flashes over between cloud and earth, canceling the difference of charge. Franklin's lightning rod—a pointed rod extending from the ground beside a house up several feet above the roof—allowed the charge on the ground to leak away so that, usually, no flash took place. If a flash did occur, the rod conducted it into the earth, so that it could not damage the house.

In the following years, Franklin studied the speed and direction of storms. He also measured the rates at which different substances conduct heat. Silver, for example, is an excellent heat conductor. Thus a silver teapot, for instance, needs a wooden handle in order not to burn the person using it.

In 1757, Franklin went to London as agent of several of the colonies. Although he continued to write on scientific subjects and to visit scientists, most of his time thereafter was taken up with travel and statesmanship. Nevertheless, even in these busy years, inventions and discoveries of many different kinds stirred in his active mind.

While living in London, Franklin visited Professor John Hadley (1731–64) at Cambridge University and helped him to measure the humidity of the air. He tried out a new electrostatic machine and invented a musical instrument, the "armonica." This instrument had a revolving shaft on which were mounted glass bowls of different sizes. The player turned the shaft by means of a treadle and brushed his fingers against the edges of the various bowls to produce musical notes. The instrument became so popular that even Mozart and Beethoven composed music for it.

During this stay in England, Franklin also wrote the first scientific accounts of the Gulf Stream and of lead poisoning. He studied the effect of a film of oil on water and towed model boats through a model canal to learn why boats move more slowly in shallow water than in deep. He devised a system of phonetic spelling; for English has one of the most confused and difficult systems of spelling found in any language. And with all this activity, he found time to send Bartram the seeds of foreign plants to see if they would grow in America.

For many years, Benjamin Franklin tried unsuccessfully to interest the British government in the grievances of the colonists. The government would not improve matters, even though the colonies threatened to break away from the mother country. At last Franklin returned to America, just as the Revolutionary War broke out. He found that the American Philosophical Society had chosen him president. He also found, among the new members, a tall, thin, shy young man named David Rittenhouse (1732–96) who, after Franklin's death, was to become the foremost scientist in the United States.

Rittenhouse was the son of a farmer whose land lay a few miles north of Philadelphia. Self-educated, he had supported himself by surveying and by making clocks and instruments. He experimented with the compressibility of water. He also invented a thermometer worked by an arm made of strips of two different metals, similar in principle to our modern thermostats. The College of Philadelphia gave the young inventor an honorary degree for this work.

For the College of Philadelphia, which grew into today's University of Pennsylvania, and for the College of New Jersey, today's Princeton University, Rittenhouse designed and built two instruments called planetaria or orreries, which are still proudly displayed by these two great institutions. An orrery is a clockwork device that shows the positions of the heavenly bodies at different dates, either by means of dials or by little balls, representing the planets circling around a central "sun." Although this kind of planetarium was named after the seventeenth-century Earl of Orrery, who owned one, devices for moving model planets by clockwork were constructed by the ancient Greeks two thousand years ago. We know this because, in 1900, the remains of one such astronomical computer were found in the wreck of a ship that had sunk in the eastern Mediterranean about 65 B.C. In more recent years, the word "planetarium" has become attached to the Zeiss projection planetarium, which shows the movements of the heavenly bodies by spots of light thrown on a domed ceiling.

For the transit of Venus across the sun in 1769, David Rittenhouse made the first American-built telescope and took part in the world-wide observations that made possible the accurate calculations of the earth's distance from the sun. Rittenhouse was also the first man to observe the atmosphere of Venus during the transit, although he did not at first realize what he had seen.

During the Revolution, Rittenhouse worked for the colonial governments as a military engineer. Afterward, he became a professor of astronomy at the University of Pennsylvania and made several important discoveries. He was the first to use a length of spider's web for the crosshairs of a telescope. He explained magnetism by saying that the particles of a magnet were themselves little magnets lined up in one direction. He made a diffraction grating—a mirror in whose surface hundreds of fine parallel grooves, close together, have been engraved for breaking up and analyzing starlight—and solved problems in optics and mathematics.

Most of these discoveries were later credited to Europeans who lived after Rittenhouse's time. The reason that David Rittenhouse was not given full credit for his work is that European scientists, knowing the backwardness of America, expected American scientists to be mere collectors of facts. They found it hard to believe that a self-educated backwoodsman could make original discoveries in a complicated science like astronomy.

After his return to the colonies in 1775, Franklin, as senior member of the Continental Congress, was too busy with the American Revolution to devote his time to science. However, when the Congress sent Franklin and John Adams to interview Lord Howe about terms of peace, Adams found himself sharing a bed in New Brunswick, New Jersey, with the famous old universal genius. Adams wanted the window closed, while Franklin preferred it open. To assure Adams that he would not catch cold, Franklin said:

"Come, open the window and come to bed, and I will convince you. I believe you are not acquainted with my theory of colds." [4]

Franklin held that colds were not, as most people thought, the result of the cool and "deadly night air," but were contagious like other diseases. He was right, of course, even though Adams fell asleep in the midst of the explanation.

During the Revolutionary War, the Continental Congress sent Franklin to France as its diplomatic agent. Although now in his seventies, Franklin continued as active in science as his failing health allowed. He invented another stove, proposed daylight-saving time, and received one of the first three air-mail letters, carried by balloon across the English Channel. Finding it awkward to change back and forth from reading to walking eyeglasses, Franklin invented bifocals.

Franklin also served on the committee appointed by King Louis XVI to look into the claims of the Austrian physician Franz Anton Mesmer (1734–1815), who said he had made marvelous cures by means of "animal magnetism." Mesmer had made a real discovery—how to hypnotize people—but he had devised a completely wrong theory to account for it. The commission, unfortunately, turned down his true discovery along with his mistaken explanation.

In 1785, Franklin came back to America, but he was not yet finished with science and invention. He experimented with fire-resistant construction in houses, and he invented a long-handled pincers for taking books off high shelves. This device continued to be used in grocery stores until the coming of the low-shelved supermarkets.

When the genial colossus finally died, Americans and Europeans alike mourned the loss of one of the greatest men of all time. Back in 1754, Franklin had published a plan for the union of the colonies. Hence, in a final tribute to this amazing American, one Frenchman stated that, besides all his other discoveries and inventions, Franklin had invented the United States of America!

III · AMERICAN EXPLORERS AND EXPEDITIONS

The science of geography began with the tales of adventures. Little by little, thoughtful men sifted through the mass of travelers' reports and gained a basic knowledge of the size and shape of the continents; of their rivers, mountains, and deserts; and of the treasures beneath the earth. Until the discovery and exploration of the Americas, however, the men of Europe held many false beliefs about the earth and its oceans.

Columbus himself caused some of the confusion. When he sailed from Spain, he set out to reach India. Because he thought that our planet was smaller than it really is and that Asia was larger, he hoped to reach the Indies by sailing four thousand miles to westward. Consequently, when he landed in the Bahama Islands, he felt sure that he had come to India and so called the natives by the misleading name of "Indians."

Although later explorers learned a great deal about the true shape and position of the American continents, they sought for geographical features that did not exist or that were less useful than they imagined. For example, men searched for a northerly passage across North America to furnish an easy route to Asia. This passage was not found until 1903–06, when the Norwegian explorer Roald Amundsen (1872–1928) sailed through it and learned that it lay too far north to be of use.

Other sailors reported a "Strait of Anian," which divided

Alaska from the rest of North America. Some even claimed to have sailed through this strait, although no such channel ever existed.

The earliest explorers of the Americas did not come to study the land and its people, nor yet to settle there. They came to carry off what treasure they could find. Having looted the capitals of the Aztecs of Mexico and the Incas of Peru, the Spanish conquistadors tramped the length and breadth of the Americas looking for more golden dream cities. They hoped to find El Dorado in South America, and, in the northern hemisphere, Quivira and the Seven Cities of Cibola. Later on, Spain, like England, sent colonists and settlers to the New World; in fact, for quite a while Spanish America was ahead of English America in civilization.

Other explorers sought the Sea of Parimá in South America and a similar inland sea said to lie in the center of North America. They sent home to Europe many facts about the land and climate of the New World; but they also told tall tales of tribes of warrior women and of headless men with faces on their chests. An eighteenth-century Turk wrote a book about America, telling of the wonderful wakwak tree, on which women grew like fruit.

Slowly, these dreams and fancies were proven false. One man who did much to sweep away the cobwebs of misinformation was Thomas Jefferson (1743–1826), author of the Declaration of Independence, governor of Virginia, minister to France, Secretary of State and Vice-President of the new nation, and, finally, the third President of the United States. Jefferson was a tall, angular, sandy-haired man of informal manner, whose great nose and long, bony jaw may still be seen on our nickels.

Like his close friend Franklin, Jefferson was an amateur architect, scientist, and inventor. As President, he filled the brand-new White House with fossils and kept a pair of young grizzly bears tethered on the lawn.

Despite the ridicule of his enemies, Jefferson collected information on weather, encouraged Jenner's method of vaccination against smallpox, and tried to find the origin of the American Indians by studying their languages. A tireless gadgeteer, Jefferson spent his spare time inventing such devices as a plow with a curved moldboard, the first swivel chair, the first shooting stick, and a drydock in which warships could be laid up in peacetime. He improved the polygraph, a copying machine for duplicating signatures; designed better music stands and writing desks; and invented a machine for processing hemp.

In the White House, Jefferson installed a dumbwaiter, a revolving clothes rack, and a set of revolving shelves pivoted in the wall for passing food from one room to another. He filled the beautiful home he designed at Monticello with original devices like a clock with two faces, one indoors and one out, and cannon-ball weights that showed the day of the week by their position. At Monticello you can still see many of these gadgets, one of the most interesting of which is a weather vane whose shaft passes down through the house to a dial on the first-floor ceiling.

In his younger days, Jefferson tried to correct some of the odd ideas that Europeans held about America. One notion was that America was a paradise inhabited by "noble savages." The other view—promoted by Georges Leclerc, Comte de Buffon (1707–88), a famous French naturalist—was that America was a wretched place where life had degenerated, where all the animals were small and the natives sluggish and stupid: a land of swamps and putrid waters overhung with deadly fogs and bordered by poisonous trees.

When he was minister to France during the American Revolution, Thomas Jefferson undertook to show Buffon the error of his view. First, he wrote to the President of New Hampshire (in those days, each state had its own president) and asked for a moose. President John Sullivan duly ordered out the troops, who shot the animal and carefully skinned it. After many delays, the huge horns and hide reached Paris. Although most of the hair had fallen off during the long sea journey, Jefferson proudly presented the bulky, malodorous remains to Buffon, who cheerfully owned himself mistaken.

Later, as President Washington's Secretary of State, Jefferson had to pass upon applications for patents. He tried to assure the new nation simple, rational systems of coinage and of weights and measures. He succeeded with the coinage but failed to oust the ancient English system of weights and measures, with its barleycorns, chains, firkins, hogsheads, links, noggins, perches, sacks, tuns, and weys.

Jefferson's system was not the French metric system, which the revolutionaries in Paris were later to adopt. It was, instead, a decimal system that he and David Rittenhouse devised. In some ways, it was better than the French system. Jefferson based the standard measure upon the length of an iron rod, which, when hung as a pendulum, had a period (the time needed to swing back and forth) of one second at latitude 45°. Jefferson divided this length into 587.5 parts, each called a "line." Ten lines made an inch, ten inches a foot, and so on up to a mile of 10,000 feet.

A committee of the U.S. Senate proposed to the British and French governments that all three countries should adopt a uniform system of weights and measures. The British and French governments, however, rebuffed the idea. After that, the short-sighted Congressmen let the idea of reform of weights and measures die for lack of interest. Since 1897, the metric system has been legal but not compulsory in the United States. Hence it is used off and on—mainly in science—along with the English system, whose inches, acres, and pounds still serve for everyday measurement.

When Jefferson became President, he sent an expedition across the unexplored continent to the edge of the Pacific. Leading the party were two Army officers: Meriwether Lewis

(1774–1809) and William Clark (1770–1838). Lewis was moody, thoughtful, and conscientious, while Clark was a genial, natural-born frontiersman. Together they made a fine team.

Before the expedition left, Jefferson consulted with the learned members of the American Philosophical Society and made up a set of questions for Lewis and Clark to answer. They were to look for the fabled Western Sea. They were to watch for live mammoths, which, Jefferson thought, might still roam the West. They were to seek for rumored marvels, such as the Great Salt Mountain, said to be of solid salt and 180 miles long.

In 1804, Lewis and Clark set out from the frontier town of St. Louis with a party of forty-five men, mostly soldiers. After wintering with the friendly Mandan Indians, they went on up the Missouri River, guided by a young Indian woman, Sacajawea. When the river became too narrow, swift, and shallow for their boats, they bought horses from the Indians and struggled over the Rocky Mountains to the land that is now eastern Washington. Thence they paddled down the Columbia River in canoes to the Pacific Ocean.

After another winter spent at the mouth of the Columbia River, they returned home by the route they had come, arriving back in St. Louis in the fall of 1806. Although they had several brushes with hostile Indians, they lost but one man: a sergeant who succumbed to appendicitis. And, while they found no Western Sea, no mammoths, no mountains of salt, they added greatly to our knowledge of North American geography.

Lewis and Clark were not the first to cross the continent. The indomitable Sir Alexander Mackenzie (1755–1820) had already tramped across Canada and, on a second expedition, had followed the river that bears his name to the Arctic Ocean. But his routes lay too far north to be important for commerce or settlement. While Lewis and Clark were out exploring,

Lieutenant Zebulon M. Pike (1779–1813) led parties of soldiers in great marches up the Mississippi to Minnesota and
across the Great Plains into Colorado and New Mexico. So began the opening of the West.

Later, John Colter, one of the men of the Lewis and Clark
expedition, went out on his own and discovered the geysers of
Yellowstone Park. The Blackfoot Indians caught him, stripped
him, and told him to run. Going barefoot over cactus, he out-
ran all but one of his pursuers, killed that one, and escaped by
diving into the Jefferson River and hiding under a tangle of
driftwood until the Indians gave up their search.

In the 1840s another Army officer, John Charles Frémont,
(1813–90), became a famous explorer. From 1842 on, he made
five long sweeps through the western states, searching for good
railroad routes. Frémont was less an explorer of completely
unknown country than a careful student of lands that had been
seen before only by wandering trappers. His lively reports encouraged and guided the westward rush of settlers.

Although Frémont was brave, energetic, and likable, he was
also rash, impulsive, and headstrong. Hence one of his expeditions ended in disaster. It got lost during the winter of
1848–49 in the mountains along the boundary between Colorado and New Mexico, and a third of his thirty-three men
perished of cold and starvation.

In 1869, John Wesley Powell (1834–1902), a professor of
geology at Illinois State Normal University, led the first expedition in boats down the Colorado River through the Grand
Canyon. This feat had been deemed impossible. Powell, a
short, hot-tempered man with a red beard, who had lost his
right hand in the Civil War, began the practice of taking parties of students on summer field trips to the West.

For his Colorado River journey, Powell assembled on the
Green River nine men and four stout rowboats. For three and a
half months they toiled down 750 miles of river, often between
towering walls of bright-colored rock and over foaming rapids

and waterfalls. One boat was smashed and another upset. Although the men got weak from hunger, they had only three casualties. These three deserted, climbed the canyon walls, and were killed by Indians who mistook them for some miners who had murdered an Indian woman.

The next year, Powell joined the U. S. Government as a member of the U. S. Geological Survey, of which he became the head. He also became head of the Bureau of Ethnology and one of the best friends of the much-abused Indians. He later made another survey of the Colorado River, with more scientific results and fewer adventures. As one modern scientist said, in speaking of expeditions: "Adventures are a sign of incompetence."

During the early years of the United States, Americans with itching feet found enough to keep them busy in North America. Then, as the continent became better known, Americans began to turn their gaze outward, to other lands and seas. Missionaries invaded Asia and the Pacific Islands; whalers and sealers ranged the Pacific and the Antarctic. In 1820, Nathaniel Brown Palmer (1799–1877), the twenty-year-old captain of the sealing sloop *Hero*, first sighted the Antarctic mainland. That is, he saw from a distance the mountains of the Palmer Peninsula. British and Russian expeditions had already explored the islands that cluster along this narrow tongue of Antarctic land.

In 1827, Jeremiah N. Reynolds, an armchair explorer from Ohio, began agitating for the United States to send expeditions abroad to explore new lands, just as parties from other civilized nations were doing. After ten years, he persuaded Congress to authorize such an expedition. However, Secretary of the Navy Mahlon Dickerson (1770–1853), disliking the project, managed to delay it for several years more by last-minute changes.

The man finally chosen to head the United States Exploring Expedition to the South Seas was the lean, lantern-jawed

Charles Wilkes (1798–1877), a stern, overbearing, intense, fearless, and self-willed naval officer. The six ships ranged from the flagship, the 780-ton sloop-of-war *Vincennes,* down to the 96-ton pilot boat *Flying-Fish.*

The expedition put out from Norfolk in 1838. About a dozen scientists (the number varied from time to time) went along. One of the smaller ships was lost in a storm while rounding the tip of South America. The party visited various Polynesian islands, where they were entertained in accordance with the elaborate Polynesian rules of etiquette.

Wilkes put his scientists ashore in Australia and took his ships south into the Antarctic wastes. After three weeks of groping through fog, storm, and ice, they sighted the Antarctic mainland and cruised along the coast as closely as the ice allowed. Wilkes later engaged in bitter quarrels over his discoveries with British and French explorers who were working in the same area at about the same time.

Reunited in New Zealand, the expedition sailed to the Fiji Islands. Here the gallant but man-eating Fijians shocked the explorers by strolling about while chewing on a joint of human limb, as if it were a turkey drumstick.

In those days, explorers from civilized countries did not consider that "savages" had any rights. A party of Americans landed on Malolo without the fierce Malolans' leave. The Americans seized the son of a chief as a hostage and, when the young man tried to escape, killed him. When the youth's father ordered an attack, in which two Americans and half a dozen Malolans were killed, Wilkes avenged the deaths of his officers by a general massacre of the natives.

After further voyaging, the expedition arrived home in 1842. It took thirty years to write the reports on the trip, and some planned volumes were never completed. The value of the publication, *Narrative of the United States Exploring Expedition,* was further diminished by the nonsensical policy of Congress, which allowed only a hundred copies to be printed.

Although British and Scandinavians have done most of the exploration of the Polar regions, American explorers have made contributions here, too. The frail and moody Elisha Kent Kane (1820–57), an officer in the Medical Corps of the U. S. Navy, went on an expedition in 1850 to hunt for the party of Sir John Franklin, which had perished in trying to sail the Northwest Passage to Alaska. Later, Kane led his own expedition between Greenland and Ellesmere Island, pushing farther north than white men had ever been.

In the 1880s, another naval officer, Robert Edwin Peary (1856–1920), began exploring around the northern end of Greenland. Between expeditions, he lectured to pay expenses. In 1909, on his sixth expedition, he became the first man to reach the North Pole itself.

Since Peary's explorations, the number of American scientific expeditions in foreign lands has grown, year by year. Nowadays, at any one time, dozens are active. They range from one-man affairs, where some lone anthropologist lives with a primitive tribe to learn how its people think, to the late Admiral Richard E. Byrd's (1888–1957) massive attacks on the Antarctic continent, with ships, airplanes, a broadcasting station, a motorboat, sledge dogs, and tractors.

Since the coming of the airplane, the surface of the earth has been almost entirely explored. Now no one is likely to discover a forgotten city where the unchanged descendants of some ancient race dwell or colossal dinosaurs and other prehistoric animals living in some lost world atop a mountain.

However, geographical exploration is but one part of the scientific investigation of the earth. There are still vast areas whose geology, fossils, smaller life forms, and people are little known. And much is yet to be learned about the depths of the oceans. One who wants to inquire into the secrets of the planet Earth, her seas, her mountains, and her primitive peoples will find work enough for many years to come.

IV · THE WORLD OF NATURE

Early explorers in America looked in wonder at such creatures as the opossum, the flying squirrel, the hummingbird, and the rattlesnake. By the time of the American revolution, a few native-born Americans had begun to take a scientific interest in the plants and animals of their country. This study of nature was called "natural history," and the students were known as naturalists.

The early naturalists set up museums for showing off specimens of wild life. Similar museums had been established in England in the seventeenth century, when certain men with collections of curiosities exhibited them to the public for a fee. Usually, when the museum owner died, his collection was sold and scattered. That is what happened to the first American museum, which was opened in Philadelphia in 1782 by the Swiss-American Pierre Eugène Du Simitière.

More important and longer-lived were the museums of the Peale family. Charles Willson Peale (1741–1827) was a Revolutionary soldier, an artist who painted George Washington and other notables, and a jack-of-all-trades. He could do almost anything. When he raised a company in the Revolutionary War, he not only commanded the men as their captain but also cooked their meals and mended their shoes. His three sons (hopefully named Rembrandt, Titian, and Raphael after three famous Old World artists) were also painters.

Peale had the collector's itch. As a result, his studio in Philadelphia soon became so cluttered with stuffed animals, including a bison, a paddlefish from the Mississippi, and an Angora cat, which Franklin had sent him from France, that he had no room left for his paintings. To solve this problem, Peale made an arrangement with the American Philosophical Society, which lent one of its rooms to him for his collection.

In 1801, Peale learned of two mastodon skeletons in a pit at Newburgh, New York. The mastodon was an extinct relative of the elephant, about as tall as a medium-sized elephant of today but more massive, with a longer body covered by coarse brown hair. Peale appealed to his old friend President Jefferson, who told the U. S. Navy to lend Peale some pumps to remove the ground water that covered the bones. Peale's first mastodon was the first mounted fossil skeleton in America and the second in the world.

Both these mastodon skeletons still exist, one in Germany and one in the American Museum of Natural History in New York. Peale's museum in Philadelphia continued in existence until 1845, when a showman named Albert Koch exhibited his famous "sea serpent" there. By stringing together the vertebrae of several specimens of a fossil whale, Koch had built up a synthetic animal 114 feet long. It was even harder then that it is now for the public to tell real marvels from fake ones.

We have already talked about some of the nation's early naturalists, such as John Bartram and his son William. In the early 1800s, William Bartram met Alexander Wilson (1766–1813), a small, dark, sad young man from Scotland who taught school near Philadelphia. To cheer up his melancholy friend, Bartram interested Wilson in the local birds.

Wilson fell in love with Bartram's niece, who taught him drawing until she married another man. Wilson, sadder than

ever, conceived the idea of composing a big picture book showing all the birds of North America. While holding odd jobs, he
tramped about the country, gathered material, and found a
publisher.

The publisher insisted that Wilson obtain the signatures of
250 subscribers, each willing to pay twenty dollars—a lot of
money in those days—for the set of eight volumes. For several
years, despite ill health and a hatred of salesmanship, Wilson
stuck to his task. He actually got several volumes published before he died of pneumonia after plunging into an icy stream to
salvage a rare bird he had shot.

One man to whom Wilson tried unsuccessfully to sell a sub-
scription was a dark, lively frontier storekeeper of French
origin. Baptized Jean Jacques Fougère Audubon-Rabin, this
man now called himself John James Audubon (1785–1851).
Audubon's father had sent him to America with money. For
some years, Audubon had lived a playboy life on an estate near
Philadelphia, where he performed the first bird-banding experiments. Young Audubon tied a thin silver wire to the leg of
each of several young peewees to see if they came back to the
same place to nest each year. He found that at least two of
them did.

Later, Audubon and a partner set out for Kentucky to make
their fortunes as frontier merchants. But Audubon proved a
poor shopkeeper. Because business bored him, he spent most of
his time in the woods, sketching and shooting birds, while his
wife kept the store. He had some close calls. Once a man with
whom he had a business dispute attacked him with a club in
the streets of Henderson, Kentucky. In spite of the fact that he
had one arm in a sling as a result of an accident, Audubon put
his attacker out of action with a stab of his dagger.

His business sense, however, got no better; and in due time
he went bankrupt. For a while, Audubon earned a scanty living
as a portrait painter and a taxidermist. Then a great idea came
to him; why not compose a large picture book about American
birds, like Wilson's, only better? Audubon's wife taught school

while Audubon gave lessons in drawing, dancing, fencing, and French to make the money for a trip to Europe.

In 1826 he sailed. The British found him a romantic figure with his lean, handsome face and long hair hanging down over the collar of his wolfskin overcoat. Charles Darwin, then a young medical student at the University of Edinburgh, heard one of his lectures on birds.

Unlike poor, dour Alexander Wilson—who never forgave Audubon for not subscribing to his work—Audubon proved an excellent salesman. He sold so many subscriptions to his book that in ten years he had paid off all his debts. After his great *Birds of America* appeared, Audubon became prosperous. He was a better artist than Wilson, although Wilson had been the keener observer of wild life. Audubon composed more picture books, traveled widely, and lived out his last years in a mansion in New York City.

In 1818, while Audubon was still storekeeping in Henderson, a strange little man called upon him. This man, unshaven and with old clothes hanging loosely about him, presented a note from one of Audubon's friends. It read:

My dear Audubon, I send you an odd fish, which may prove to be undescribed, and hope you will do so in your next letter.[1]

The man was Constantine Samuel Rafinesque (1783–1840), born in Turkey of French and German ancestry. He was a more brilliant naturalist than either Wilson or Audubon but so peculiar and unworldly that he never succeeded at anything. Audubon later described him in print under a false name as an "eccentric naturalist." As Audubon was fairly eccentric himself, you can imagine the sort of man Rafinesque was. He traveled about the country looking for new species to describe, supporting himself by odd jobs between times. His enthusiasm for new species of mammals, birds, reptiles, and fish amounted to a mania.

When Rafinesque and Audubon had talked natural history

far into the night, they went to bed. Then an uproar brought Audubon to his guest's room. He found a naked naturalist leaping about and swatting at three bats with the shattered remains of Audubon's violin, all the while shrieking that the bats belonged to a new species.

Audubon, an expert fencer, killed the bats with the bow of the violin. Then, irked by the loss of his fine fiddle, he played a fiendish joke on Rafinesque. He drew pictures of weird imaginary fishes and passed them off on Rafinesque as real fishes from the Mississippi. Rafinesque duly published reports about them, giving them long Latin names.

Rafinesque later got a professorship in Lexington, Kentucky, but made so many enemies that he soon lost his job. He drifted back to Philadelphia, where he dabbled in writing, lecturing, inventing, and banking until he died in obscure poverty.

A contemporary of Audubon and Rafinesque was Thomas Say (1787–1834), a handsome, pleasant, personable descendant of John Bartram. In 1812, Say helped to found the Academy of Natural Sciences in Philadelphia. For years he lived in the Academy's rooms, eating twelve cents' worth of the plainest food per day, in order to study natural history instead of following the career of apothecary in which he had been trained.

Say was the first American to make a scientific study of American insects. Becoming known as a naturalist, he went on several expeditions: one to Florida, another to the Rocky Mountains, and a third to the land west of Lake Superior. The second expedition, in 1819, was headed by Major Stephen H. Long (1784–1864). Say was appointed zoölogist, with Titian Peale, of the painting Peales, as his assistant.

The expedition was no great success. It failed to find Pikes Peak and the source of the Platte River. Moreover, Say and his companions were robbed, once by Indians and once by the soldiers sent along to protect them. To round things out, Congress cut off the expedition's appropriation, so the explorers had to struggle along on what supplies and equipment they had already bought.

Say spent his later years at New Harmony, Indiana, as a member of a coöperative society founded by the Scottish reformer Robert Owen (1771–1858). Owen, a textile mill owner, thought that by setting up a colony with a perfect, democratic constitution, people could be persuaded to give up all their selfishness and other faults and to create a peaceful, harmonious society. About a thousand persons—many of them of intellectual distinction—gathered at New Harmony in 1826 for the great experiment. Alas for Owen's fine plans! The idealists quarreled furiously, plotted and intrigued against one another, and broke up into hostile factions. After only two years, the community changed itself into an ordinary incorporated village.

Nevertheless, because of all the brain power that had been concentrated there, New Harmony continued for some years as a scientific center, with an importance out of proportion to its size. All four of Owen's sons became Americans of distinction. The eldest, Robert Dale Owen (1801–77), in the course of a long and successful political career, drafted the bill setting up the Smithsonian Institution.

The youngest, David Dale Owen (1807–60), became the nation's leading geologist. The strange house in New Harmony, which he used as a laboratory, still stands, looking something like the upper story of a Norman castle, with a fish-shaped weather vane flying from one of the turrets.

The Academy of Natural Sciences in Philadelphia was one of many organizations that sprang up in the early nineteenth century to make knowledge available to everybody who wanted to learn. Lecture centers called lyceums became very popular, until by 1835 over three thousand towns had such institutions.

Many of the lectures in the lyceums were on natural history,

BUTTERFLY CATCHING IN THE EARLY NINETEENTH CENTURY

which became a popular hobby. Gentlemen in tight trousers and tall beaver hats and ladies in coal-scuttle bonnets and billowing skirts bounded through the fields of America waving butterfly nets. A house guest was sure to be shown the host's collection of insects pinned to a board.

Later on in the nineteenth century, natural history broke up into separate sciences, as the number of facts known about the world of nature became too great for any one man to master. Trained scientists called biologists took over most of the work in these new sciences. In the late nineteenth and early twentieth centuries, the older, less scientific naturalists came more and more to be represented by men who wrote popular books and articles on the beauties of nature. These included Henry David Thoreau (1817–62), the Massachusetts philosopher; John Burroughs (1837–1921), the popularizer of the nature essay; John Muir (1838–1914), the man most responsible for Yosemite National Park; and Ernest Thompson Seton (1860–1946), the founder of the Boy Scouts of America.

Some of these writers, like Burroughs, wrote more or less truthful accounts of the doings of wild animals. Others, like the Rev. William J. Long, wrote fantastic tales of snakes avenging their slain mates, porcupines shooting their quills, gorillas kidnapping African women, and other beasts talking, bringing up human children, sacrificing themselves for their young, and obeying human laws and rules of behavior. None of these things, of course, happens in real life. President Theodore Roosevelt, himself an able zoölogist, denounced these "nature fakers" in scorching terms.

During the nineteenth century, many American cities acquired museums of natural history, such as the Chicago Natural History Museum and the United States National Museum in Washington, D.C. The greatest of all of these is the American Museum of Natural History, standing west of Central Park in New York. After the Civil War, a naturalist from

Maine, Albert Smith Bickmore (1839–1914), persuaded a rich New York importer named Theodore Roosevelt, father of the President of that name, to help him promote such a museum for New York City.

Roosevelt got together a number of bankers and business-men, who formed a board of trustees. They agreed with the city that the trustees should pay for the collections and their care, while the city should furnish the land and the buildings. The cornerstone of the first building was laid in 1874, in the presence of President Grant and other notables. Joseph Henry of the Smithsonian Institution made a speech in which he stressed the importance of a museum as a teacher of the people.

Yet, as teachers of the people, early museums left much to be desired. The exhibits were crowded, badly lighted, and ex-plained by labels printed in type too small to read and lan-guage too technical for most museum visitors to understand. The American Museum of Natural History not only has grown to enormous size but also has led the world in the new-est techniques of educating its visitors. Only about one tenth of its specimens are on display in the halls. The rest are kept in reserve for study. If they were all shown at once, the museum would be so crowded that the visitor would be more confused than enlightened.

Much of the growth of this museum is due to two men. One was the banker J. Pierpont Morgan (1837–1913), a big domi-neering man with a walrus mustache and a nose like a red banana. Although many of Morgan's critics denounced him as a wicked old pirate for his ruthlessly selfish financial deals, Mor-gan served American science well. He bought whole collections and gave them to the American Museum of Natural History. For example, he gave the Star of India, the world's largest cut star sapphire, to its mineral collection. Moreover, for years he bullied his fellow bankers into making up the museum's defi-cits.

The other man was Henry Fairfield Osborn (1857–1935), an eminent American paleontologist, or student of fossil animals. Fossils are the remains of long-dead animals and plants, dug out of the earth or cut out of the stone that formed around them. By studying fossils, we have learned much about the climate, the land, and the life on earth millions of years ago.

The son of a railroad president, Osborn got up a private fossil-hunting expedition to the West while he was still a student at Princeton. Later he became a professor at Columbia University and president of the American Museum of Natural History, which he ably managed for twenty-five years.

Osborn was a tall, mustached man of regal dignity. Although some people disliked his pompous manner, his scientific achievements were unquestioned. He wrote huge books on the ancestry of various animals, such as elephants. He invented the modern method of describing the teeth of mammals, with special names for all the bumps and hollows. He prophesied that the elephant's ancestors would be discovered in Africa and proved his theory in 1907 by finding fossils of these piglike animals in Egypt. During Osborn's long, distinguished presidency of the American Museum of Natural History, this museum grew to be the largest of its kind in the world.

Of the many expeditions that Osborn sent into the field, the most famous was the Third Asiatic Expedition of the American Museum of Natural History, which went to Mongolia in the 1920s under Roy Chapman Andrews (1884–1960). Despite the hazards of driving trucks and automobiles across the roadless Gobi Desert and the harassment of soldiers and officials sent out by the Chinese and Soviet governments, the expedition found the first eggs definitely known to be those of a dinosaur.

It also uncovered the remains of the largest known land mammal of all time, a hornless rhinoceros called Baluchitherium, which looked like a monstrous tapir, one and a half times the size of an elephant. It found the largest flesh-eating land mammal, Andrewsarchus, a hyenalike carnivore thrice the size of a grizzly bear, and uncovered many other fossils of great importance in unraveling the history of life on earth.

Another man who had much to do with the growth of the American Museum of Natural History was the taxidermist, sculptor, and naturalist Carl E. Akeley (1864–1926). As a young man, Akeley worked for the taxidermist Henry A. Ward in Rochester, New York. At that time "stuffed" animals were really stuffed, with straw, old rags, or anything handy. The mounted beast appeared to be just what it was: namely, an animal's skin stuffed with straw.

Ward had a contract with P. T. Barnum, the showman, to mount the skin of the famous elephant Jumbo after Jumbo died. Jumbo died in 1885 as a result of a collision with a train. Since the specimen was much too large for the usual stuffing job, Akeley mounted the skin on a frame of steel and wood.

Later, when Akeley was working for a museum in Milwaukee, he further improved his method of mounting animals. Akeley's new method was to prepare a manikin, modeled to resemble the living animal with all its muscles and other organs. Then the skin was stretched over this manikin.

Akeley found that, to make a lifelike clay model, he had to be both a sculptor and an expert on the anatomy of the species he was mounting. Moreover, he could not mount the skin directly on the clay model, because the clay mount would deteriorate. He had to make a plaster-of-Paris mold of the model, coat the inside of the mold with glue, and build up, inside the mold, a manikin of muslin, shellac, and papier-mâché, reinforced with wire cloth. When a part of the manikin had been finished and dried, it was separated from the mold by dissolving the glue in water.

Later, Akeley mounted four groups of deer in the Field Museum in Chicago, showing the animals as they appeared in the four seasons. These groups established the new principle of surrounding the animals with faithful copies of their natural dwelling places, complete with proper soil and plants. Nowadays a museum sends artists and taxidermists to a particular site to paint and photograph the scene and to collect plant specimens. At the museum, molds are made from the real leaves of typical plants, and waxen casts are made from these molds and painted. Real leaves would turn brown and shrivel up.

For some years, Akeley collected specimens for the African Hall of the Field Museum—now the Chicago Natural History Museum. Once a leopard, which he had stunned with a shot that glanced off its skull, revived as Akeley examined it. Although fearfully chewed, Akeley succeeded in strangling the leopard to death. Another time an elephant tried to run him through with its tusks. Akeley got caught between the tusks and was saved from being squashed between the animal's trunk and the ground only because the tusks struck a root or stone beneath the soil.

Later, Akeley collected animals for the African Hall of the American Museum of Natural History, the finest of its kind in the world. He was still collecting specimens when he died on a safari in 1926, ten years before the hall he created was opened to the public.

In colonial America, there were few people but plenty of land and resources. As a result, Americans became very fussy about saving the lives of individuals but very wasteful of natural resources. Settlers on the frontier cut down every tree in sight and shot every animal that moved. In the late nineteenth century, the government encouraged hunters to wipe out the bison, or buffalo, which had roamed the western plains in millions. This was done so that the Indians, who depended on the animal for food, would be reduced to starvation or confined to reservations. Accordingly, by 1890, only about 2,000 bison were left.

Some thoughtful men realized that, at this rate, many of the nation's resources would be permanently exhausted and most of its wild life exterminated. At the same time, the human population was increasing at such a rate that it would some day crowd the nation to overflowing. Eventually, there would not be enough resources to go around.

Moreover, they thought that a country which had been completely settled, tamed, and built up, with neither wilderness nor wild life, would be a dull and dismal place to live. Therefore, they campaigned against this reckless destruction of natural resources. So began the conservation movement in the United States.

One conservationist, the naturalist William T. Hornaday (1854–1937), raised such an uproar about the vanishing bison that the animals were at last protected. They have now increased to over twenty thousand, most of them in Canada. Other scientists—notably David Starr Jordan (1851–1931), the first president of Stanford University—saved the Alaskan fur seal from extinction. This required long negotiations with the governments of Canada, Japan, and Russia, whose sealers had been mercilessly hunting the animals.

In the 1880s, women decided to wear beautiful feathers or whole birds on their hats. To meet this demand, hunters brought several species of birds, such as the Florida egret, to the verge of extinction. To save the birds, George Bird Grinnell (1849–1938), who had been a pupil of Audubon's wife, founded a series of Audubon Societies in 1886. These societies, devoted to the study and protection of birds, are still active today.

The most effective conservationist of all was the younger Theodore Roosevelt (1858–1919)—vigorous, versatile, brilliant, opinionated, and one of three United States Presidents who can be called real scientists. (The other two were Thomas Jefferson and Herbert Hoover.) When Roosevelt became President, he withdrew the government's coal and iron lands from sale to private interests, tripled the area of the national forests, and made ranchers pay for letting their cattle eat the government's grass.

After Roosevelt had completed his years as President, he went to Africa to collect animals for the National Museum in Washington. Later he explored an unknown river in Brazil. One man of his party drowned; another murdered a member of the expedition; and Roosevelt nearly died of an infected foot. But the party struggled through 900 miles of wilderness, and the river was renamed the Río Roosevelt after its explorer.

Following Theodore Roosevelt's second term in the White House, conservation efforts by the government lagged for many years, until President Franklin D. Roosevelt vigorously revived them in the 1930s. Although, after the latter's death in 1945, interest in conservation again declined, many modern Americans are becoming aware of the alarming waste of our natural resources and the urgent need to protect trees, plants, minerals, and animals if we want our children's children to inherit a beautiful and useful land.

V · EARLY INVENTORS AND INVENTIONS

Centuries ago, inventors had a hard time. People who liked the old-fashioned ways or who thought that a new invention might harm their business often urged the passage of laws to stop the use of the invention. If they could not obtain such a law, such people might even attack the inventor or damage his machines with stones and clubs.

Later, people came to realize that inventions make life easier and pleasanter and therefore should be encouraged. The most practical way of encouraging invention is to give the inventor a *patent*. A patent is a legal monopoly on the invention; it gives the inventor the sole right to exploit his invention for a definite number of years.

So, for a certain time (seventeen years in the United States), the owner of a patent has the right to stop all others from making, selling, or using his invention without his permission. If anybody does so, the patent owner can sue him for infringing his patent. The profits that the inventor makes during the life of his monopoly are supposed to repay him for the cost, effort, and risk of developing the invention. Patents for inventions were first granted in fifteenth-century Italy.

The practical-minded American colonists thought better of inventors than they did of pure scientists—that is, men who pursued scientific information for its own sake rather than for

48

practical results. Even so, early American inventors found life difficult. For one thing, there were no patent offices or, indeed, any regular system for granting patents. An inventor had to ask the government of his colony to pass a special law giving him a monopoly. The first of these colonial patents was granted in 1641 by the Massachusetts General Court to Samuel Winslow for a method of making salt. In 1646, the same court gave Joseph Jenks the first American patent on machinery—a mill for making scythes.

Jenks was one of the workers at the Saugus Iron Works, which John Winthrop, Jr.—the man who brought the telescope to the colonies—had caused to be built northeast of Boston. For their time, the Saugus Works were very up-to-date, with several huge water wheels working the bellows of the smelting furnaces and the heavy trip hammers that shaped the raw iron. The Saugus mill produced iron in square ingots called "pigs," in sheets, and in rods that farmers bought in bundles to make into nails.

The Saugus works flourished for about twenty years. Then bad management and the competition of cheaper English iron caused the works to lose money. About 1670 they were abandoned and fell into ruin. A city grew up around the site. In the 1950s, a group of American iron and steel companies gave money to buy up the land, tear down the homes, and restore the famous old iron works. Today Americans interested in history can see the machinery operating just as it did three hundred years ago.

The lack of a proper patent system was not the only problem of early American inventors. Most of them knew but little pure science, because very little science was known and less was taught in America. Worse yet, most inventors had no idea what other inventors were doing in the same field. Hence they were always duplicating each others' efforts and repeating each others' mistakes.

They did not know that one man seldom creates an entirely new invention all by himself. Most major inventions are made by a series of inventors, each adding his improvement to the original idea. For instance, there is really no one inventor of the steamboat. Jouffroy, Fitch, Evans, Symington, Stevens, and Fulton all had a hand in the final result. Only a few important inventions, such as Thomas A. Edison's phonograph, Whitcomb L. Judson's slide fastener (the "Zipper"), and George Westinghouse's air brake have been wholly originated by a single man.

Furthermore, the early American inventors did not realize what a long, hard road stretches from the first original idea to the final, workable, profitable invention. When one of them got a hopeful idea, he imagined that his fortune was already made. He thought a few weeks of tinkering would whip the device into shape. He thought that he was the only man ever to have such a wonderful idea, and that any rival inventor must be a liar and a thief. As he was usually wrong on all counts, it is no wonder that he had his troubles.

American inventors also suffered from the technical backwardness of their country. Not only were there no engineering libraries or institutes of technology; there were not even machine shops where the inventor could have the parts of his engine accurately tooled. So the inventor had to do his own mechanical work, and woe unto him if he were not handy with hammer, file, chisel, drill, lathe, and other tools!

Despite these handicaps, Americans have always loved gadgets. In the colonies, clockmakers made clocks with brass works and fancy dials for the rich, and with wooden works and plain faces for the common folk. Housewives had home-made wooden eggbeaters, apple parers, meat mincers, and other labor savers. Swiss and German immigrants developed the Pennsylvania rifle, which helped the colonists to win the Revolution, since it far outranged the inaccurate and sightless British musket.

In 1787, the Constitutional Convention launched that daring, radical experiment called the United States of America. The new Constitution allowed Congress "to promote the Progress of Science and useful Arts by securing for limited Times to Authors and Inventors the exclusive Right to their respective Writings and Discoveries." Thus was the U. S. patent system born.

The first patents were granted by a board made up of the Secretary of State, the Secretary of War, and the Attorney General. The first patent, issued July 31, 1790, gave Samuel Hopkins a monopoly on a method of making potash. The patent was signed by President George Washington, Attorney General Edmund Randolph, and Secretary of State Thomas Jefferson. The second patent went to Joseph Simpson for a method of making candles.

The third patent taken out under the new Constitution was granted to a stout millwright from Delaware, Oliver Evans (1755–1819) for an "Improvement in Manufacturing Meal." Evans was one of the most active inventors of the new republic. His most important inventions were in milling machinery. He applied not only for United States patents but also for several state patents, because some states still issued them. In some of these, he included a design for a steam wagon. Pennsylvania made him take the steam wagon out of his application on the ground that he must be mad to think of such a thing.

Nevertheless, in 1805 Evans built an amphibious steam dredge to dig the sediment out of the harbor of Philadelphia. Evans ran the dredge from his shop to the water on wheels, rolled it into the river, hooked up a stern wheel, and sailed about for some hours before setting the dredge to the work for which it was meant. Although there had been experiments with steam-driven wagons and boats, this was certainly the world's first powered vehicle that could move both on land and on water.

Evans died after a life of struggle, many disappointments,

and some small success. After his death, the U. S. Supreme Court held one of his milling-machine patents to be no good, because it did not clearly point out Evans's contribution as compared with what had been done before.

As a result of this decision, when a new patent law was passed in 1836, it required that each patent have a set of "claims." These are little numbered paragraphs at the end of the description of the invention, setting forth just what the inventor thinks is new about his invention.

The first man to make a boat move by steam was Claude F. Dorothée, Marquis de Jouffroy d'Abbans (1751–1832), a Frenchman who got the idea while serving a jail sentence for dueling. In 1783, Jouffroy's steamboat chugged along the Saône River for about fifteen minutes. Then it sprang so many leaks that Jouffroy had to run it aground to keep from sinking. Because the French Revolution drove him from his native land before he could perfect his boat, the scene of steamboat invention shifted to America.

The most active steamboat inventor after Jouffroy was John Fitch (1743–98), a native of Connecticut who had already led a checkered career before he went into inventing. He had abandoned his wife; had deserted from the Continental Army in the Revolution; had made a fortune profiteering and lost it by inflation; had been captured by Indians and held prisoner by the British throughout the latter part of the war; and had worked as a silversmith and a mapmaker.

Of all the steamboat inventors, Fitch had the most brilliant ideas. Part of his failure was due to lack of money and education, and to the general backwardness of the country. But in part he failed because of his own nature. He was so nervous, excitable, haughty, quarrelsome, and impractical that he never got on with the men he worked with.

Fitch built several steamboats in Philadelphia. The first was driven by twelve steam-powered oars. The third, the *Persever-*

ance, had paddles hanging over the stern which kicked the boat along, like a swimming duck, at eight miles an hour. For one season, in 1790, Fitch ran this boat commercially on the Delaware River, between Philadelphia and Trenton. Although the boat worked fairly well, it failed to make a profit. For one thing, it competed with the best roads and the fastest coach lines in the United States. For another, it was so full of machinery that there was little room left for paying passengers.

The next winter, when a storm pulled the boat loose from its pier and grounded it downstream, Fitch could not afford to salvage it. After a fruitless trip to Europe to try to raise money and to get machinery for another boat, Fitch wandered off to Kentucky and took his own life.

Fitch had been fighting a war of pamphlets, petitions, and lawsuits against a rival inventor, James Rumsey (1743–92). Rumsey's boats, which sucked water in at the bow and squirted it out astern, like a squid, were by no means so good as Fitch's; but Rumsey was much cleverer at persuading men with money to back him. He was in England building one of these boats when he died in 1792.

For the next several years, people tinkered with steamboats without much success. Those who came closest to a workable design were John Stevens, Jr. (1749–1838), a New Jersey lawyer, and William Symington (1764–1831), a Scotch engineer. Symington's boat, a tug driven by a stern paddle wheel, would probably have proved successful had not the Scot's financial backer unexpectedly died.

The first man to make a steamboat run and also earn a profit was Robert Fulton (1765–1815), an artist and inventor from Pennsylvania. Fulton had spent several years trying to interest the French and British governments in his ideas for submarines and submarine mines.

His submarine was an improved version of one invented by David Bushnell (1742?–1824) of Connecticut. Bushnell's

American Turtle was a one-man craft that looked like a big buoy. It had two screw propellers worked by cranks from within, one to push the craft horizontally and one to raise and lower it. Although a marvel of ingenuity, Bushnell's submarine failed to damage the British fleet during the Revolutionary War.

Fulton, trying to sell his underwater craft to Napoleon, made equally fruitless attacks on British warships blockading the French port of Le Havre. (A bit of an adventurer, Fulton had no objection to blowing up bystanders in his quest for a fortune.) In France, he fell in with Stevens's brother-in-law, Robert R. Livingston (1746–1813), the American minister to France. Livingston, who had unsuccessfully tried his hand at inventing a steamboat, suggested a partnership to Fulton.

Back in America, Livingston obtained a franchise to run steamboats on the Hudson River, while Fulton imported a Watt steam engine and built his boat in New York. The ship developed into a slender side-wheeler with a tall structure rising amidships to carry power from the cylinder to the paddle wheels. Although Fulton called his craft the *North River Steamboat,* it came to be known as the *Clermont* after Livingston's riverside estate.

On a summer day in 1807—August 17—Fulton made his first passenger-carrying run from New York to Albany. People flocked to the river bank to watch the great experiment. As the novel craft steamed by, many spectators cheered; but one farmer ran to his cabin shouting that the Devil was going up the river in a sawmill.

As soon as he returned from this famous run, Fulton improved his steamboat in the light of experience—for there were many errors in the original design—and put it into regular service. He made money from the start, because he plied a long route between two great cities, which were connected only by terrible roads but which fronted on a splendid river. Although the river lacked towpaths for hauling and good winds for sail-

**EXPERIMENTAL VESSELS OF THE AGE OF THE INVENTION
OF THE STEAMBOAT**

Top: Evan's amphibious dredge, the *Orukter Amphibolus* (1804-5); *Middle:*
One of Fitch's early steamboats (1786); *Bottom:* Fulton's man-powered
submarine (1801).

ing, it was deep and straight, with no falls or rapids—a perfect body of water for steam navigation.

Fulton kept improving his steamboats as long as he lived. He built twenty-one in all, each an advance on the last, carrying boilers made by Paul Revere, the Boston silversmith. They included the world's first steam warship, the "floating battery" *Demologos*.[1] This ship had a brilliantly original design. She was a catamaran—a boat with two hulls, side by side—with the engine and the boiler below the waterline, one in each of the twin hulls, and a single paddle wheel turning in the space between them. Besides conventional artillery, her armament included such inventions as underwater guns to punch holes in the enemy's bottom at close range, and a nozzle for squirting boiling water on the enemy's deck. Her sides were of oak five feet thick, making her practically an armored vessel.

Fulton's boats worked exceptionally well because he drew such accurate and beautiful pictures of each of the parts he needed that his mechanics had little trouble in making them exactly right. Although Fulton was not *the* inventor of the steamboat, as he himself sometimes admitted, he did more than any other man to develop it. Less of an original genius than Fitch, he was far shrewder in raising capital and in managing his business affairs. He was an inventive, energetic, poised, likable, and not overscrupulous fellow who was out to make his fortune by any means available and who succeeded in doing so.

In 1793, a large, dark, hook-nosed young man from Connecticut arrived in Georgia to undertake a tutoring job that a fellow Yankee, Phineas Miller, had obtained for him. His name was Eli Whitney (1765–1825).

Two species of cotton then grew in the South. One was sea-island, or long-staple, cotton, the fibers of which were attached loosely to slippery black seeds. The other was short-staple, or upland, cotton with fibers of two different lengths, the shorter

tightly fastened to green seeds. Long-staple cotton, which grew
only along the sea coast, could be separated from its seeds by
running it through a roller frame something like an old-
fashioned clothes wringer. The Southerners called this device
an "engine"; but, as the years passed, careless speech had
shortened the word to "gin." Upland cotton could be grown
over a vastly larger area than sea-island cotton—but, unfortunately, the only way to separate its fibers from their seeds was
by laboriously picking out the seeds by hand.

Whitney invented a machine for removing the seeds from
upland cotton, the basic part of which was a cylinder turned
by a crank. From this cylinder, hundreds of bent wires (later
developed into saw-toothed disks) stuck out like fingers. These
pieces of wire moved through slots wide enough for the cotton
but not wide enough for the seeds. As the cylinder turned, the
hooks pulled the cotton through the slots, leaving the seeds behind. Finally, a revolving brush removed the cleaned cotton
from the cylinder.

With Phineas Miller as his partner, Whitney took out a patent and began exploiting his invention. Although the gin was
an immediate success, it was long before the partners made any
profit on the device. The gin was so simple that any clever
blacksmith could construct one. Therefore the Southern plant-
ers, who cared little for patents and laws, built their own machines and ginned their own cotton. When Whitney demanded
that they pay him his royalties, they defied him. It took years
of Whitney's and Miller's time and thousands of dollars in lawsuits to collect even a modest profit on this very important invention.

The cotton gin greatly affected the history of the United
States. Around 1800, the world's more civilized nations had
either abolished slavery or were about to do so, and there was
much feeling against slavery in the United States. Most of the
Founding Fathers disapproved of it. The Declaration of Independence was full of noble words about the equality and rights

of men. The Constitution laid upon Congress the duty of maintaining a republican government in the United States—meaning a government with no hereditary ruling classes.

Whitney's gin, however, made the growing of upland cotton by slaves very profitable, since the operations were all simple acts that an illiterate slave, with no hope of getting anywhere in the world, could do perfectly well. As a result, the Southern states became more than ever devoted to slavery. It took the Civil War to put an end to the institution; and even now, over a hundred years later, the principle that all men shall be treated equally is not fully established everywhere.

According to the original patent law, the Secretary of State issued patents in person. With the growth of the nation and the increase in invention, this became impractical. Therefore, in 1836, the U. S. Patent Office was organized, with a Commissioner of Patents at its head.

Unfortunately, in the last month of that year, a fire destroyed the Patent Office and all its records. For several years, the Patent Office occupied itself with restoring its records as best it could; but, because of the fire, no copies of certain early patents exist. Today so many copies of every patent are printed that it is hard to imagine a similar disaster.

As we have seen, nearly all inventions are improvements on something that already existed. When one inventor holds a patent on an invention, and another patents an improvement on that invention, who has the right to what? This question was answered shortly after Elias Howe (1819–67) invented the sewing machine.

Howe, a mechanic and instrument-maker of Boston, solved a problem that for years had perplexed inventors. He mechanically imitated the movement of the human hand in sewing, by combining the action of two needles with eyes near their points, working from opposite sides of the fabric. Then he obtained a patent on his invention.

For a long time, Howe had little success in marketing his machine. In 1849, however, several manufacturers began to make sewing machines more or less like his. Howe sued the most successful of these manufacturers, Isaac Merrit Singer (1811–75), for infringement of his patent.

As a result of his suit, the courts ruled that one man may patent a basic invention; another may patent a clear-cut improvement on it. Thus both inventors are protected. Howe had a valid patent on the basic idea of the sewing machine. Singer had a valid patent on certain improvements on that machine. Howe could stop anybody, including Singer, from making the machine itself. Singer could stop anybody, including Howe, from making the machine with Singer's improvements.

Luckily, Howe and Singer were men of sound judgment. Instead of fighting to the death over the question of who was the "true" inventor—as did so many rival inventors in those days —they agreed upon a contract. Under this contract, Singer paid Howe license fees for making sewing machines covered by Howe's patent. The other manufacturers accepted similar contracts with Howe, who was thus enabled to spend his last years in comfort.

Since the time of Howe, the patent system has grown enormously. Whereas in 1839 the Commissioner asked Congress to increase the examiners from two to four, the Patent Office now has over a thousand examiners. It has granted more than three million patents in all and nowadays issues them at the rate of about 40,000 a year.

With millions of patents—including thousands of important ones—already issued, and more coming out of the Patent Office every week, a whole library of books would be needed to describe every American invention. However, the principles of patent law, under which these patents are still issued and enforced, are the same principles worked out in the first half-century of the nation's existence.

Although not perfect, the American patent system is still the fairest and most practical method yet discovered for encouraging and rewarding inventors. And this encouragement of invention is perhaps the main reason why our modern scientific civilization has sprung into being in less than two hundred years and why Americans are considered the most inventive people on earth. Each country has its own patent system, and they all differ. In France, for instance, applications for patents are not examined for newness. The patent is issued automatically, and the question of novelty is brought up for the first time when the patent owner tries to enforce his monopoly. The different systems have various advantages, but on the whole the United States system seems to work best.

VI · THE GREAT INDUSTRIAL REVOLUTION

We all know that our homes, our clothes, our roads and cars, even our daily newspapers are very very different from those of George Washington's time. We have handy inventions to serve us, such as central heating, electric lights, and washing machines. We can travel much faster and can communicate with each other more quickly because of the steamboat, railroads, airplanes, telephones, and radios. We have seen how the earliest of these inventions came into being as a result of a flowering of scientific discoveries that started in the sixteenth and seventeenth centuries, of the fact that each invention opened the door to other inventions, and of the growing protection of inventors by patent laws in Europe and America.

Today, material things—articles of manufacture—are made in vastly larger quantities and at much lower prices than was once the case. For the first time in the world's history, ordinary people can enjoy comforts and conveniences that ancient kings would have envied. The wealth of goods we see in every department store are there for us to buy because of a great change in methods of production that has been taking place during the past two hundred years. This change, which began in England in the eighteenth century, we call the Industrial Revolution.

The Industrial Revolution was actually made up of a number

of changes that occurred in rapid succession. In earlier times, most craftsmen were self-employed and made articles by hand in their homes, with the help of their children or of young boys to whom they taught their skills. Then, in the 1760s, the first factories were built in England to house textile machinery run by water power. At first men and women, then even small children, had to go to work in these factories, where they did specialized routine jobs day after day for small wages.

Another change occurred. The power of engines—steam engines and, later, internal combustion engines—was added to the power of wind, water, and muscle. As more factories were set up, more complicated machines were invented to handle raw materials, to shape parts, and to combine the parts into finished products.

In colonial America there were clockmakers, cabinetmakers, gunsmiths, carpenters, wainwrights, and blacksmiths. Most of them were not even full-time artisans, but farmers who practiced their mechanical arts in the off season. In European towns at that time, workers were a little more specialized. They worked at their craft all day and bought their food from local shopkeepers. But a clockmaker still made a whole clock; a gunsmith, a whole gun; and so forth.

After the Industrial Revolution, each man made but a single part, or ran a single machine that performed one operation. True, a modern workman gets less satisfaction out of tightening nut number 51 on the assembly line, over and over, day in and day out, than his forerunner got from making a complete article. Yet, under the new system, a given number of men can turn out many more articles each day; and thus the workman and his family can afford many household luxuries his forerunner could never have hoped to own.

The factory system began with a number of English inventions that mechanized the making of cloth. In 1733, John Kay's flying shuttle vastly speeded up the looms that wove thread into yard goods. The spinning machines of Hargreaves, Arkwright, and Crompton, later in the century, enabled one operator to spin a large number of threads at once. Dozens of other inventions helped to build a huge textile industry in the north of England, even before the coming of Watt's steam engine.

British laws against manufacturing by Americans long kept the factory system from taking root in the colonies, since, according to the theory of the British government, colonial people should not be allowed to do or make anything that would endanger the livelihood of those who stayed home. After the Revolution, the British government could no longer keep Americans from setting up their own factories; but they hindered the growth of such factories as much as they could by laws that forbade British mechanics to leave their own country.

In 1789, Samuel Slater (1768–1835), an apprentice to a partner of Arkwright, decided to emigrate in spite of the laws. To avoid suspicion, he carried no papers, no drawings of textile machinery. He did not need drawings because he had memorized all the details of the latest British textile machines. As manager of the factory of Almy and Brown at Pawtucket, Rhode Island, he soon had the plant humming. From then on the factory system spread throughout the northern United States.

As power-driven machines grew larger and more complicated, men had to discover and harness new and more powerful forms of energy. Muscle, wind, and water had long been used in manufacture and transportation. Medieval Europeans had learned that a large windmill could do as much work as three water wheels, or twenty-five horses, or three hundred men. But, as men and horses were too costly and the wind too uncertain, such industrial power as the American colonists used came mainly from water.

SLATER'S TREADMILL USED TO PROVIDE POWER FOR THE FIRST
TEXTILE MILL IN PAWTUCKET, MASSACHUSETTS

Colonial water wheels for turning grain mills and hammering iron were set up along the "fall line," where swift streams descended the slopes of the Allegheny Mountains to meet the flat coastal plain. These wheels were of the simple overshot and undershot types (that is, the water ran over or under the wheel) that had been used for centuries.

In the 1820s, a young French engineer, Benoît Fourneyron (1802–67), invented a much more efficient water wheel, called a turbine. Fourneyron's turbine took much more energy from a given stream of water, flowing at a particular rate, than a water wheel of the older types. However, turbines did not reach their full importance for another sixty years. Water wheels, no matter how efficient, had to be placed where water flowed swiftly, and these places were often far from centers of population. Until the development of the electric generator and motor, there was no way to move the energy of the water wheel to the place where it was needed.

In the United States, the first working combination of a water wheel and an electric generator was made by Lester Allen Pelton, a mechanic who drove an oxcart from Ohio to California during the Gold Rush of 1849. As a mining engineer in Nevada in 1880, Pelton faced the problem of getting power from a small waterfall, which was a third of a mile high, to a stamping mill—a machine for crushing ore—over a mile away.

Pelton solved the problem by building a water wheel of his own design. It had a nozzle that squirted water against a double circle of curved buckets set around the rim of the wheel. The water turned the wheel; the wheel turned a generator to make electric current; and the current ran through wires to the mill, where it turned an electric motor. The Pelton wheel is used to this day where water pressure is high but volume is low.

As the United States outgrew its supply of water power, other sources of energy were sought. Josiah White, a Philadelphia ironmonger, opened up the great beds of Pennsylvania anthracite coal in the 1810s and 20s, although he had a struggle to persuade people that this "black stone" would really burn.

Ever since the coal fields of the Alleghenies were put into use, most of the power generated in the United States has come from coal. The next most important source is petroleum—a natural oil pumped out of the ground. Edwin L. Drake began pumping oil in western Pennsylvania in 1859. The chemist Benjamin Silliman, Jr. (1816–85) discovered how to break up petroleum into the oils, gases, waxes, and tars of which it is a mixture.

At first petroleum was pumped and refined largely for the mixture of light oils called kerosene. Early in the nineteenth century, a form of home lighting better than candles had been discovered and had become quite popular in the more settled areas of the nation. This was the whale-oil lamp. But whale oil was costly and hard to come by; so, before the time of the Civil War, the more readily available kerosene largely replaced whale oil and put an end to the dangerous but colorful whaling industry of New England.

Fifty years later, when automobiles came into use, the petroleum industry welcomed them gladly. For the automobile engine burns a still lighter mixture of petroleum oils, called gasoline, which had formerly been a useless, flammable by-product of the making of kerosene. As the heavier oils came to be burned in the furnaces of steam engines and, later, in diesel engines, today no part of the valuable source of energy that men have called "black gold" goes to waste.

At the same time that new sources of energy were being developed, new machines capable of running more efficiently on these fuels were being invented. The engine that made the Industrial Revolution possible was the steam engine.

Although a toy steam engine had been built in the first century after Christ by Heron of Alexandria, the steam engine as we know it originated in England. In the seventeenth century, many mine shafts had been driven so deep into the earth that they filled up with ground water. To get rid of this water, steam pumps were invented. About 1712, Thomas Newcomen (1663–1729) improved these "fountain engines" by adding a vacuum cylinder in which a piston moved up and down.

In 1765, James Watt of Glasgow (1736–1819) was struck by an idea for an even better engine. In Watt's engine, the steam, instead of being condensed in the cylinder by a jet of cold water, was condensed in a separate chamber. This engine could do as much work as Newcomen's vacuum engine on only one third as much fuel. At the time of the American Revolution, there were only a couple of Newcomen engines in the colonies. Watt's steam engine was known, although none yet existed in America.

Watt's engine worked only at very low steam pressure. Other engineers, in Great Britain and the United States, soon realized that the steam engine would work more efficiently—that is, it would give more power per pound of fuel—if it ran at a higher pressure. This change involved some risk; for, with the crude boilermaking methods of the time, a boiler was likely to blow up if put under too much pressure. Little by little, men learned to make boilers to withstand high pressures.

One of those who experimented with high-pressure steam engines was Oliver Evans, who built the amphibious steam dredge. Even more important to the Industrial Revolution than his high-pressure engines, however, were Evans's improvements in milling machinery. He used power-driven machinery, not merely to act upon a raw material, but also to carry it around the factory.

In Evans's mills, grain and flour were conveyed about the mill by belt conveyors, screw conveyors, hoppers, and similar devices. Most of these machines had been used before in handling liquids, but Evans was the first to use them to move solids. This idea is the basis of modern assembly-line, mass-production manufacture. Evans's mills were the first step towards the modern factory, wherein machines do all the heavy work and the workers merely tend the machines.

Evans never had much success with his mass-production mill, because he was trying to change the methods of an old, established industry that did not wish to be changed. Only a few daring experimenters like George Washington took out licenses under his patent to build similar mills.

Another experimenter with high-pressure steam engines was a New Jersey lawyer and inventor, John Stevens, Jr. (1749–1838). Stevens had tinkered with steamboats before Fulton built his *North River*. Not being handy with tools, Stevens had to hire mechanics and had bad luck with them. So he brought up his son, Robert Livingston Stevens (1787–1856), to know all the mechanical arts.

In 1802, they put together a not-too-effective boat powered by a primitive high-pressure steam turbine, which drove a screw propeller. Later, Stevens built a more conventional steamboat, the *Phoenix*, as a rival to Fulton's ship and designed an iron-clad warship.

Stevens also introduced into America the railroad, which had been developed in England. This proved a technical advance of the utmost importance to the youthful United States. Stevens ran a toy steam engine around his estate and took part in chartering the Pennsylvania Railroad. In 1832, at the age of eighty-three, he put his own railroad, the Camden and Amboy, into operation in New Jersey.

Stevens's whole family proved gifted in engineering. His son Robert made a number of railroading inventions, including the T-rail, the wooden cross tie, the railroad spike, gravel ballast for tracks, and the pilot truck for locomotives. He also invented the false bow for ships and designed the cup-winning yacht *America*. Another Stevens sent, at his own expense, an ironclad gunboat of his own design to serve the Union in the Civil War. For many years, the mansion that the Stevenses built on a hill in Hoboken was part of Stevens Institute of Technology, a technical college that they founded to train other engineers.

Thanks to the efforts of men like the Stevenses, railroads soon covered the settled parts of the United States. During the Civil War, for the first time in history, railroads played an important part in moving troops behind the lines. By 1869, the first rails stretched across the continent to the Pacific.

In the early days of American railroading, cities were connected by many little railroad lines built to at least six different gages or width of track. To travel even a short distance, as from Albany to Buffalo, one had to change trains several times.

When railroads were built to the Pacific, pressure from railroad interests led Congress to fix the gage at the British standard of four feet, eight and a half inches. This British gage in turn was based upon the gage of mine cars and may go back to the gage of ancient Roman chariots. Thus, possibly, the width between the wheels of Roman chariots has now become standard for most railroads of the world, including those of the United States.

While Eli Whitney was fighting the infringement of his cotton-gin patent in 1798, he got a contract from the U. S. Government for ten thousand muskets. These were to be finished by September, 1800. When the time came and no muskets had been delivered, the War Department began to worry.

To persuade the Department to extend his contract, Whitney took a number of musket locks to Washington. Before a group of officials, he took the locks apart and mixed the parts. Then, taking up parts at random, he astounded his audience by putting a complete lock together and showing that it worked.

What was so surprising about this? In earlier times, every machine was made up of parts fitted together by hand. No two machines of a given model were exactly alike, because the parts of which they were made varied from one to the next. If you took a part from one machine and tried to use it in another machine of the same model, it probably would not fit.

Whitney had made a remarkable invention: the principle of

interchangeable parts, a vital step toward mass-production methods. Whitney's parts were made on machines whose motions were guided, not by the hands of men, but by jigs and templates, so that each machine went through exactly the same motions and produced identical parts. Thus a great deal of time was saved in assembling the final product, because any set of parts would fit together. Although two Frenchmen, Leblanc and Brunel, had already pioneered these methods, Whitney and his English contemporary Joseph Bramah (1748–1814), an inventor and manufacturer of locks, were the first to put them into practice on a large scale.

Needless to say, Whitney got his contract extended by Congress and soon thereafter produced excellent guns for the soldiers of the new nation. After Whitney died, his son carried on the business, which grew into the Winchester Arms Company. In the 1840s Samuel Colt (1814–62), inventor of the Colt revolver, improved Whitney's methods of mass production still further by assigning each of his workers to a single, simple operation, which the man performed over and over.

The British first realized the importance of mass production when American products were shown at the Crystal Palace Exposition in London, in 1851. Overlooking the work of their countryman Bramah, the British government sent a commission to the United States to study the American system of making interchangeable parts.

Machinery to help the farmer was also coming into being in the middle of the nineteenth century. One exhibit at the Crystal Palace was McCormick's reaper, which the London *Times* described as a "cross between an Astley chariot" (a kind of carriage), "a wheelbarrow, and a flying machine." [1] A young Virginian, Cyrus Hall McCormick (1809–84), had developed the device in the 1830s with the help of his father and an ingenious Negro slave, Jo Anderson.

In this machine, a revolving "reel," like that of a lawn

mower, pushed the wheat back against a pair of toothed steel strips, like saw blades. One of these strips jerked swiftly back and forth against the other, cutting the wheat in the same way that the barber's clippers cuts hair. Although most of the parts of the reaper were already known, McCormick combined them in this way for the first time.

McCormick, an able, aggressive individualist, moved to Chicago and built up his business. Here he fought many battles with his rivals; for competition was so rough that salesmen even tried to disable their competitors' machines before a trial. The reaper greatly helped the Union to win the Civil War by releasing, for service in the armies, thousands of men who otherwise would have had to stay home to work as farm hands.

McCormick's reaper was not the only machine to mechanize agriculture in the nineteenth century. Machines to bind and thresh wheat also came into use. The work of European chemists showed that certain simple chemicals could be combined to make artificial fertilizers. These synthetic fertilizers fostered the growth of plants quite as well as animal products and could be had in much larger quantities; thus the productivity of each farmer was again increased.

In 1874, an American, Joseph Glidden, patented barbed wire. This invention vastly simplified the fencing problem of the farmer and the rancher. However, Glidden's barbed wire came close to having an adverse effect on all future American inventions, because he decided to enforce his patent by suing, not only the infringing makers and sellers of wire, but also the users of the illegally made fencing. Hence, many outraged farmers rushed to their Congressmen, demanding that the patent system be done away with. Luckily, their demands went unheeded and inventions are still protected by law.

At the end of the century, the tractor, driven first by steam and later by a gasoline engine, began to take the place of the horse for plowing and hauling. Today, in the United States, the tractor has almost entirely displaced the horse for farm work.

In short, an Agricultural Revolution followed in the wake of the Industrial Revolution, with the result that relatively few farmers can now feed the rapidly growing population of our nation.

Science and invention played a much greater part in the Civil War than in any earlier war. Joseph Henry, the Secretary of the Smithsonian Institution, pursued researches into military inventions. In 1863, Henry helped to organize the National Academy of Sciences to give technical help to the Union.

The Union put some of the first repeating rifles into its soldiers' hands. The Confederates complained that, with these new guns, a Yankee could "load up in the morning and shoot all day." If the war had lasted longer, the Union would also have had the first machine gun in action. This gun, invented by Richard J. Gatling of Chicago (1818–1903), was fired by turning a crank.

The Confederacy raised a sunken Union warship, the steam frigate *Merrimac*, and armored her with railroad iron, after removing the masts and sails that ordinary steam warships still carried.

Hearing of this monster, the Federal government turned to John Ericsson (1803–89), the leading American engineer of his day. Born in Sweden, Ericsson was a bald, long-armed man of enormus physical strength. He cared for little but his engineering and was likely to sleep on a desk in his office when working hard. In England he built a locomotive and invented the steam fire-engine and the hot-air engine. He was also one of the inventors of the screw propeller for ships.

Moving to the United States in 1839, Ericsson set himself up as a shipbuilder. To fight the Confederacy's armored ship, now renamed the *Virginia*, Ericsson built a ship called the *Monitor*, of an even more radical design. This was a low, flat-decked craft. In the middle rose a single revolving turret housing two guns. Ericsson invented the turret and the ammunition hoist that lifted powder and shot from the hold to the guns.

On March 9, 1862, the *Monitor* fought the *Virginia* to a standstill at Hampton Roads and kept the Confederate ship from breaking the Union blockade. Throughout the rest of the war, both sides built armored ships as fast as they could. From these ships, our modern warships evolved.

One of the many reasons for the defeat of the Confederacy was that the leaders of the Union, from President Lincoln down, realized the importance of science and invention in war, while the leaders of the Confederacy did not. Although the Confederacy had brilliant inventors, who tried out ingenious ideas for submarines and underwater mines, the political leaders did not understand technical matters and gave their inventors small help.

The new machinery being built in America required enormous amounts of steel. Steel is a refined alloy made from iron, and it is the most widely useful form of iron.

Nearly all commercial iron has some carbon dissolved in the metal. If the carbon is less than one-quarter of one per cent, the iron is called wrought iron. It is, as iron goes, soft but tough. If the carbon makes up more than 1.7 per cent of the mixture, the iron is called cast iron. It is hard, stiff, and brittle. If the carbon content is between .25 and 1.7 per cent, it is called steel. Steel has greater strength and springiness than either wrought iron or cast iron.

The process from which modern steel-making grew was invented by William Kelly (1811–88), a Pittsburgher who tried being a traveling salesman, a tobacco farmer, and finally an ironmonger in Kentucky. In 1846, he found that he could make molten iron still hotter by blowing cold air through it. When he told his wife this, she thought him mad and called the doctor. The physician, an intelligent man, listened to Kelly's explanation and sided with the ironmonger.

The reason for this curious effect is that the oxygen in the air blown through the iron combines with the carbon and other impurities in the iron. When other substances combine with oxygen, they *burn*. So the stream of cool air burns the impurities out of the iron, and the burning makes the molten mass hotter than ever. Ten years later, the British inventor Sir Henry Bessemer (1813–98) made the same discovery.

Kelly got a U. S. patent on his air-blowing process, while Bessemer got a patent on the egg-shaped vessel, pivoted so that it could be tipped, in which steel-makers carried out the process. As neither man could use the other's invention without permission, the industrialists who had bought the rights to Kelly's process merged their company with that of the men who had bought the right to use Bessemer's converter; and the mighty American steel industry was on its way.

For thousands of years, since the beginnings of civilization, men had made their houses and bridges of wood, brick, and stone. Using only these materials, some splendid structures had been built. Nevertheless, wood, brick, and stone are weak in tensile strength; that is, they cannot stand much *pull*. Most metals—especially steel—are much stronger in tensile strength. The weakness of the older materials meant that buildings were limited in height and interior space, and bridges were limited in span.

The ancient Greeks and Romans made a few experiments with beams of bronze or iron in their temples, but they soon dropped this idea because of the cost of the metals. In medieval India and China a few suspension bridges were built that were held up by iron chains. The use of iron in bridges was revived in eighteenth-century Europe, when a suspension bridge supported by iron chains was built in 1741 in England. The first all-iron bridge appeared in the 1780s. Abraham Darby III, of a famous iron-smelting family, built at Colebrookdale an arched bridge with five cast-iron ribs assembled on the site.

Throughout the nineteenth century, arch, truss, and suspension bridges, made first of iron and later of steel, became more and more common both in Great Britain and in the United

States. One of the most famous of these bridges was a three-arch steel railroad bridge across the Mississippi at St. Louis, which was built by James B. Eads (1827–87) during the years 1867–74, and which is still in service.

While working on this bridge, several men died of caisson disease, commonly called "the bends." The bends occur if a man comes to the surface too quickly after working in high-pressure air in a caisson at the bottom of the river. When a man leaves high-pressure air too quickly, the air dissolved in his blood forms bubbles, just as the gas in a soft drink does when the bottle is uncapped.

Eads and his physician, Doctor Jaminet, traced the source of the trouble. In order to prevent injuries from the bends, they insisted on giving the men physical examinations before letting them enter the caisson. Then they limited the time their men were allowed to spend under pressure, and they brought them back to the surface slowly. The principles they worked out still apply to diving and other underwater work today.

A suspension bridge held up by wire cable was first built in France in 1836, but the most striking advances in bridges of this kind were made by the Roeblings, a family of German-American engineers. After building several wire-cable suspension bridges in the Midwest, John A. Roebling (1806–69) was authorized in 1867 to construct the famous Brooklyn Bridge. Two years later, while surveying the sites of the piers, John Roebling was fatally injured when his leg was crushed between a boat and a pier. His son, Washington A. Roebling (1837–1926), took over the job of chief engineer and completed the great bridge.

During the sinking of the foundations for the piers, the younger Roebling was crippled by caisson disease. Nevertheless, he directed the work from his sickroom until the bridge was finished in 1883. Since then, many large suspension bridges have been built in America, with spans ranging up to the 4,200 feet of the Golden Gate Bridge in San Francisco.

Builders were slower to use iron and steel in houses than in bridges. Nevertheless, the use of these metals began to spread after the middle of the nineteenth century, when the Kelly-Bessemer process made steel much cheaper than before. At first, iron columns and beams were substituted for wooden ones to make the building fireproof rather than stronger.

Then, for the Exposition of 1851 in London, Joseph Paxton built the Crystal Palace, a building made entirely of iron and glass, which led the way to modern skyscraper construction. Not to be outshone by her sister metropolis, New York determined to have a Crystal Palace, too. The American copy was destroyed by fire only five years later. Although the glass and iron did not burn, the exhibits went up in roaring flames; and the heat melted the glass and buckled the iron. The London Palace stood until 1936, when it suffered a similar fate.

Despite this disaster, American architects began to realize the possibilities of steel beams. Several Midwesterners, among whom were William Le Baron Jenney (1832–1907), Daniel Hudson Burnham (1846–1912), and Louis Henri Sullivan (1856–1924), developed the new method of construction. Jenney's ten-story Home Insurance Building, completed in Chicago in 1885, is considered the world's first real skyscraper. In office buildings of this kind, the walls carry little or no load. The load-bearing part of the structure is a cagelike skeleton of steel beams, to which sections of flooring are attached.

Although buildings were now able to soar skyward, few people cared to risk heart failure by climbing more than a few flights of stairs at a time. Therefore, even with new methods of construction, tall buildings would have been impractical had it not been for another invention: the elevator. The first elevators, built around 1850, were worked by water pressure and carried freight from one story to that just above or below it. The car was mounted on the upper end of a long plunger, which extended down into a close-fitting cylinder. When a valve was opened, water, let into the bottom of the cylinder under pressure, forced the car up. Another valve let the water out and allowed the car to descend. The valves were worked by cables, which ran through holes in the floor of the car. The operator seized one of these cables with a heavy glove and tugged at it to make the elevator rise; he seized the other cable to make it descend.

Since the cylinder of the hydraulic elevator had to extend down into the ground as far as the shaft extended up, the hydraulic elevator in its original form could not serve buildings over two or three stories high without a cost too high to be practical. Longer and swifter movement of the car was next obtained by making the hydraulic cylinder separate from the car and connected with it by a system of pulleys and cables, which multiplied the motion of the cylinder.

But cables wear out, and the elevator was still not safe enough for passengers until, during the 1850s, Elisha G. Otis (1811–61) invented an automatic brake, which stopped the descent of the car the instant the rope holding it up went slack. By 1857, Otis had installed one of his elevators in a five-story building. About the same time, steam-powered elevators also appeared. In the 1880s and 90s, elevators were electrified. The American pioneer in this field was Frank J. Sprague (1857–1934), who also invented the multiple-unit electric train, and who perfected his electric elevator in 1892. The electric elevator makes it possible to whisk passengers up fifty or a hundred stories.

Manhattan, built on hard rock and surrounded by water, proved an ideal place for skyscrapers. Rivers kept the business districts from expanding outward, while the rock provided a strong foundation. As New York's buildings pushed skyward, her architects turned for decoration to the columns of Roman temples and the spires of medieval cathedrals, so that early skyscrapers were cluttered with these ornaments. For example, the Woolworth Building, which was completed in 1912 and which remained for nearly twenty years the world's tallest office building, has Gothic pinnacles like those of a cathedral.

In the 1840s, an American sculptor living in Italy set forth an important theory of architecture. This man was Horatio Greenough (1805–52), who is also remembered for a colossal seated statue of George Washington, wearing only a Roman toga loosely draped about him. For many years, this statue was hidden away in the cellars of the Smithsonian Institution, because the sight of the half-naked torso of the Father of his Country embarrassed many of his countrymen.

Greenough's architectural theory proved of the utmost importance. Called "functionalism," it may be summed up in the sentence: "Form follows function." Greenough meant that a building would be beautiful if it was designed to do its work efficiently. There was no need for fussy ornamentation; in fact, such additions detracted from the artistic whole.

Since the days of Jenney and Sullivan, skyscrapers have become steadily taller and more capacious. In accordance with Greenough's theory, they have also become simpler in design. New York's height-zoning law, which requires buildings to be set back above a certain height, has turned many skyscrapers into modern ziggurats, those great brick step-pyramids which the ancient Babylonians attached to their temples.

From the United States, skyscrapers have spread all over the world. They are fine in cities where space is precious; but occasionally skyscrapers have been built where there was no real need for them, simply because this style of building had become fashionable. In a small town, for instance, a new skyscraper may lure all the tenants out of the older buildings, causing heavy losses to the owners of the older buildings and thus damaging the town's economy.

Because so many new office buildings look like nothing but glass bricks standing on end, some people think that Greenough's functionalism and the use of glass have both been overdone. When a building consists so largely of glass, light and temperature inside become hard to control. Despite Venetian blinds and air-conditioning, workers are dazzled by glare, roasted by summer suns, and frozen by winter winds.

By the end of the nineteenth century, the world George Washington knew had to a large degree become the sort of world we know today. New engines, new fuels, and steel could be had in quantity; machine tools turned out interchangeable parts; and power-driven machines moved materials about the factory. Several steps remained to be taken to perfect the process of mass production—the making of standardized articles cheaply and in quantity.

One thing was assembly-line manufacture, which was developed to its fullest extent by the American automobile industry. Although the automobile first evolved in Europe, Henry Ford (1863–1947) and his engineers worked out methods of putting automobiles together as the parts moved along on power-driven assembly lines. These lines flowed together, like the tributaries of a river, carrying the ever-growing sections of a car until the last bolt was inserted and a completed Model T Ford rolled off the assembly line.

Each man on the line did one operation over and over again. The work was simple; but it was monotonous. The workman had to move in time with his fellows in order not to hold up the whole line. Moving in time all day is very fatiguing and uninspiring.

Other improvements in methods of manufacture resulted from studying each job in order to find out how each man could work more efficiently and then training him to use this efficient method of work. Studying jobs in this way is called efficiency engineering or scientific management. Scientific management was worked out by a Philadelphian, Frederick Winslow Taylor (1856–1915).

Taylor began his career as a laborer for a steel company. He worked his way up to chief engineer while putting himself through college by evening study. A champion tennis player in his youth, he was a small blond man whose mild manner covered a fiery temper. Taylor, who rattled out arguments like a machine gun, and who constantly overworked, was a talented inventor in the field of metal-working. Intense, self-assertive, stubborn, uncompromising, and so abstemious that he would not even drink tea or coffee, his only vice was swearing. While nobody could call him an easy man, his drive was exactly what was needed to put American factory management on a scientific basis.

Taylor's method was, first, to watch a worker at his job, timing every one of the man's movements with a stop watch. By careful study, Taylor learned to arrange a man's surroundings so that he could turn out more work without working any harder. This was done by placing his tools or the controls of his machine so that he could reach them more easily, without bending or stretching. Furthermore, his routine was so arranged that while at his bench he did not have to get up, move around, or run errands.

Taylor also worked out standard routines for lubricating machines; for he found that when each worker was allowed to oil his own machine in any way he liked, several bearing surfaces were likely to be skipped. He devised systems for keeping track of tools borrowed from the tool room; and, when he absent-mindedly forgot to return a tool, he fined himself just as if he had been one of the workers.

Taylor was not the first man to try to make factories more productive. Many others had designed improved machines to save labor and had trained the machinists to apply their efforts more effectively. A British mathematician and computing-machine inventor, Charles Babbage, had even published a book on the subject in 1832. Taylor, however, not only proposed reforms in management, but, unpopular as these reforms were, also made them stick.

Taylor encountered much opposition to his reforms. When he began his studies, American national self-conceit was at its peak. Most factory people were so convinced of the superiority of all things American that they scoffed at the idea that their methods could be improved. Many workers opposed Taylor's ideas because they feared that the system would merely be used to speed them up without giving them any increase in pay. This was not entirely an idle fear. Many managers ignored Taylor's warning that, when his system was installed, the workers must be given a fair share of any resulting increase in profits or the thing would not work. Taylor had even more trouble with managers who did not wish their own accustomed routines changed, or who did not want to go to the trouble of carefully planning their operations in advance. Taylor's methods became so unpopular that for several years Congress put in its appropriation bills a ban on Taylorism in government offices.

Little by little, Taylor's methods came to be accepted, until at last they were in common use in every well-run firm. They have now so completely passed into the fabric of American life that the housewife who plans her kitchen in order to get through her work with the fewest steps never stops to think that she is applying Taylorism. Yet Taylor's methods are still unknown to many people in other parts of the world.

A number of men who called themselves efficiency engineers followed Taylor. Many were able; but there were some fakers among them who promised vast improvements and accomplished little. Of the able ones, one of the best-known was Frank B. Gilbreth (1868–1924), who worked his way up from a bricklayer. Two of his twelve children collaborated on a hilarious book about their father, *Cheaper by the Dozen.* They told how he saved seventeen seconds out of every day by lathering his face with two shaving brushes, one in each hand. Then he tried shaving with two razors at once; but at this point the system broke down. Gilbreth found that he lost more time in bandaging his cuts than he saved by using two razors. Even efficiency, he learned, can be overdone.

The Industrial Revolution began about two hundred years ago and is not yet complete. So far, three giant steps have been taken: (1) bringing men together in factories to work in coöperation; (2) making machines do the work of men; and (3) arranging this work so that the men who guided the machines could do so with the least effort. Another and final step, still under way, is to make the machines guide themselves—adjust themselves, lubricate themselves, and feed themselves with raw materials. When such machines are built, the worker no longer runs the machine. He merely starts it and watches it to make sure it is working right, since any machine breaks down sooner or later. This final step is called "automation."

The first attempt at automation was made in 1725 by Basile Bouchon, a French mechanic. Bouchon invented a loom in which a roll of perforated paper, like that of a player piano, passed under a box full of sliding pins. At each stage of the work, the pins were all dropped down on the surface of the paper. Those that met paper were stopped while those that met holes went on through. Since the pins were connected to the threads of the loom, the pattern of the holes in the paper controlled the pattern of the cloth to be woven. A machine of this kind came to be known as the Jacquard loom, after Joseph Marie Jacquard (1752–1834), who in 1801 built an improved loom on Bouchon's design.

Bouchon's loom was not the only source of automation. Another kind of self-regulation appeared in Edmund Lee's English windmill of 1745. Before Lee, a windmill could be kept face to the wind only by constant effort on the part of the miller, who turned the turret by means of a crowbar or a winch. Lee invented the fantail or fly. This was a little auxiliary wind wheel mounted astern of the turret, with its shaft at right angles to that of the main wind shaft. The fantail was connected by cables or gearing with a wheel on the ground or a gear on the post carrying the movable part of the mill.

As long as the windmill was aimed straight into the wind,

the wind struck the vanes of the fantail edgewise, so that it did not turn. As soon, however, as the wind shifted, it caused the fantail to spin, turning the turret until it again faced to windward.

The next step in self-regulation of machines was the fly-ball governor—that is, a device to *govern* the speed of an engine—invented by James Watt in 1787. This governor had two or more balls on the end of hinged arms, which were mounted at the top of a shaft driven by the engine. As the shaft whirled, the balls flew outward, raising the arms. The faster the engine went, the more nearly did the arms rise to a horizontal position. But, as they rose, they closed a throttle valve, slowing down the engine. Thus, once the governor had been set for a certain speed, it would keep the engine very close to that speed in spite of changes in steam pressure.

Another early step toward making machines more self-operative was Oliver Evans's automatic flour mill, which had its conveyors for moving grain around the building. Still another step was taken by Eli Whitney, whose jigs and dies enabled his machine tools to repeat the same motions as often as desired. Thus, little by little, during the last century and a half, machine operation has been made ever more automatic and self-regulating.

Along with increasing automation has come the development of data-processing machines which compile information and feed instructions into machines without constant human supervision. The first step in this direction was the invention of the punch-card sorting machine by Dr. Herman Hollerith, a statistician with the U. S. Census Bureau.

In the late nineteenth century, with the swift growth of the nation, the Census Bureau found itself falling farther and farther behind in completing its ten-yearly reports. The census figures had to be entered by hand on millions of cards, which in turn had to be sorted and re-sorted by hand. Hence the results of the 1880 census were not published until 1887. It looked as if the Census Bureau would soon be conducting one census before the results of the previous one had been made known.

Hollerith invented a machine that worked on the principle of the Jacquard loom. He used, first, a roll of perforated tape and, later, separate punched cards. A set of telescoping pins descended on each card in turn. Where a pin found a hole, it went through and into a tiny cup containing mercury, thus closing an electrical circuit.

Hollerith's machines were first tried out in 1890. By 1900, when they had been further perfected, they reduced the time needed to tabulate the census data to a year and seven months. Hollerith went into business for himself, and the company he founded grew into the huge International Business Machines Corporation. Nowadays, punched cards and tapes are used to control all sorts of complicated manufacturing operations.

The Industrial Revolution, which began in England, flowered in the United States during the nineteenth and twentieth centuries. It has brought greater changes into the lives of people in the United States than anywhere else in the world and has raised the American standard of living higher than that of any other nation.

Before this great change began, a man made each article all by himself, in his own home or shop, using tools powered by his own muscles. In the factories of the nineteenth century, a man ran a power-driven machine that made one part of a product. He started and stopped the machine, saw that it was correctly adjusted, and fed raw materials into it. In a twentieth-century automated factory, machines start and stop themselves and feed themselves raw materials, while a single man oversees a whole assembly of machines. Sometimes, he merely mans a bank of signal lights that flash on when a machine develops trouble. He may even watch his distant machines on closed-circuit television screens.

Each advance in mechanization and automation has forced workers out of the jobs to which they were accustomed and has thus caused severe hardships for workers who were too old, or not adaptable enough, to learn new trades. But although, for some families, technical changes have brought poverty and problems, the Industrial Revolution has increased the wealth and welfare of the average American many times over.

Why did the Industrial Revolution so enrich the people of the United States, when many other nations that also had generous resources and clever citizens, failed to advance so far? There is no single reason for the swift progress of industry in the United States. Our industrial progress depended in part on the fact that the nation was not overcrowded. People were few compared to the vastness of the land, and labor costs were consequently much higher than in densely populated countries. Because wages were higher, factory owners found it profitable to buy labor-saving machinery as fast as it was invented.

The nature of the American government and society also encouraged industrial progress. Our government is based upon the idea that men are equal, at least in legal right; and that a man should be allowed to rise in the world as far as his abilities permit, with no artificial barriers of class to hold him to one fixed station in life. These ideals do not always work perfectly in practice; nevertheless, people with bright ideas for inventions, new enterprises, and improvements in industrial methods have had more encouragement than similar men have had in many other lands.

Finally, because the United States was in itself a daring experiment, Americans have perhaps been more eager to try out new methods and new products than people in more conservative parts of the world.

PART TWO
The Physical Sciences

VII · THE EXACT SCIENCES

It is hard for people born in the twentieth century to realize the full impact of the Industrial Revolution. The coming of the machine age has changed the life of every living person; for, even in the most distant corners of the globe, modern tools, weapons, medicine, education, and knowledge of science have undermined the old ways and furnished the pattern for the new.

The Industrial Revolution was followed by a whole series of related revolutions—in transportation, in agriculture, in methods of building, and in ways of life. Along with these developments went an explosion of ideas and a whirlwind of changes in social conditions. During the twentieth century, scientific knowledge has grown so fast and discoveries have traveled from country to country so swiftly that science has become an international affair, with little regard for national boundaries.

As we have seen, America was late in developing a strong interest in scientific research, although Americans have always been fascinated by gadgets and delighted to tinker with inventions. As we shall see, American science caught up with European science early in the twentieth century. Since that time, American scientists have pressed ahead so fast that today our country leads the nations of the world in money spent on research, in number of working scientists, and in number and diversity of discoveries and inventions.

Science falls into two main categories: *pure science* and *applied science*. Pure science considers how the universe works and how life has developed into the plants and animals we see on earth today. By means of pure science (such as chemistry, physics, geology, biology, or astronomy) we learn the laws of nature, the way the bodies of beasts and men are constructed, and how the minds of men function. Applied science, often called engineering or technology (such as civil, mechanical, electrical, or chemical engineering), puts the laws of nature to practical use in building better structures and machines for the comfort and convenience of men.

When a man learns some new fact by research in pure science, we say that he has made a *scientific discovery*. When he puts an earlier discovery to some practical use, in a new and original way, we say that he has made an *invention*.

In the two hundred years since the beginning of the great change that we call the Industrial Revolution, developments both in pure and in applied science speeded up in a way that the world had never seen. All the sciences leaped forward, neck and neck like horses in a race. At one time, one pulled ahead; then another caught up with and passed it. An invention in one field made possible some discovery in another; and that discovery, in turn, permitted another new application of science for the benefit of man. For example: the invention of the microscope led to the discovery of germs; eventually, the germ theory of disease made possible the curing of many ills for which no effective treatments had ever before been known.

From early scientific discoveries and inventions have evolved whole new branches of scientific endeavor. Pure science has been subdivided into the *physical sciences,* which deal with the facts and relations of the physical world, and the *biological sciences,* which investigate the history and workings of life on this planet. A special branch of the biological sciences, often considered apart from them, consists of the *social sciences*, which deal with the behavior of men and the workings of their societies. As time passes, each science splits into more and more branches or subdivisions.

In the nineteenth century, so many discoveries and inventions took place in various fields of science that the physical, biological, and applied sciences split up into many narrower, more specialized subdivisions. No longer could any one man learn all there was to know about an entire field or science, such as physics or biology; he had to specialize in order to master even a part of the fast-growing body of fact in his own particular area. The increasing speed of scientific development will be obvious if one considers that television, space craft, and nuclear-powered ships, which are taken for granted now, would have seemed fantastic to people whose lives ended as recently as 1920.

As new developments followed hard upon the old, as the discoveries of one genius furnished the key to further inventions, as teams of specialists worked to solve the remaining mysteries of the universe, the story of science in America became a far more complicated tale than the straightforward account of discovery and invention in the time of Benjamin Franklin.

Therefore, from this point on, we shall have to consider the various branches of science one by one in order to learn their history. At the same time, we should remember that the scientific developments in one field are closely related to the developments of the same time in other fields. For instance, Willard F. Libby, the physicist who worked out the method of radiocarbon dating of ancient relics, affected, as you will see, the sciences of anthropology, archaeology, and geology. Furthermore, scientific developments have influenced political history, as when the invention of the cotton gin made large, slave-owning plantations profitable in the South and so played a large part in bringing about the Civil War. Likewise, political events in different parts of the world have affected the course of science in America, as when Hitler's persecution of the Jews caused many brilliant physicists to flee to America.

Because the strands of our scientific history are so closely intertwined with those of our political history and with the inventions and discoveries being made in Europe, the reader will be wise, now and then, to turn to the table at the end of this book and study the time chart of events. This chart should make it easy to see that events described in different chapters are, nevertheless, merely different strands in the interwoven fabric of our machine-age civilization.

In the nineteenth century, the United States made many important contributions to the Industrial Revolution, and the results of American invention and engineering came to be known far and wide. In pure science, however, the United States long lagged behind the leading nations of Europe; it even trailed the backward Russian Empire. Despite its one universal genius, Franklin, and several lesser lights like Rittenhouse, the youthful nation was a scientific wilderness.

So lacking were scientific knowledge and techniques that, in 1804, when Professor Benjamin Silliman ordered a dozen glass chemical retorts from a New Haven glass maker and sent the two parts of a broken retort as a pattern, he received twelve new retorts with the necks carefully broken off in the same place as in the sample.

Silliman had just become professor of chemistry and natural history at Yale, because the college had decided to establish the professorship and young Silliman was available. When Silliman was told of the appointment, he protested:

"But I am not qualified for such a position!"

President Dwight of Yale replied quite honestly: "That is of no matter; neither is anyone else we can think of in this country." [1]

Silliman met the challenge, making many minor but valuable investigations into such subjects as mining, sugar-cane growing, and the oxyhydrogen blowpipe. His real importance, however, lay in his teaching and organizing of scientists, in founding scientific publications (one of which became the influential *American Journal of Science*), and in spreading public respect for science by popular lectures. His son Benjamin Silliman, Jr. (1816–85) was the noted petroleum chemist.

American backwardness was especially marked in such exact sciences as mathematics, physics, and chemistry. This was a natural result of early American liking for the practical and profitable, and scorn of mere theory. In these sciences, the most precise and penetrating thought was needed; the practical benefits were not so clear.

Higher mathematics had a few followers in the young republic. One of these was Nathaniel Bowditch (1773–1838) of Salem, Massachusetts. Bowditch taught himself Latin in order to read Newton's *Principia*, went to sea, worked up to captain, made money, and went into the insurance business. While at sea, he rewrote a British seaman's handbook, Moore's *Practical Navigator*, in which he had found many errors. Bowditch's book, *The New American Practical Navigator*, ran through many revisions and is still in use. He also translated from the French the first volume of the Marquis de Laplace's *Celestial Mechanics*, the first major scientific work ever published in the United States.

A young man named Benjamin Peirce (1809–80), who read the proofs of Bowditch's translation of Laplace, later became a professor at Harvard and the nation's leading mathematician. Among other things, he founded that branch of higher mathematics called linear associative algebra. He also sired two sons, James Mill Peirce (1834–1906) and Charles Santiago Sanders Peirce (1839–1914), both of whom became mathematicians in their turn. Charles Peirce founded a system of philosophy, which he called "pragmatism." A cousin of the family, Benjamin Osgood Peirce (1854–1914), was the author of *Peirce's Table of Integrals*, known to every engineering student today.

After Benjamin Peirce, the two leading mathematicians in

the United States were Newcomb and Sylvester. Born in Nova Scotia, Simon Newcomb (1835–1909) became a professor of mathematics in the United States Navy. Because, at that time, the Navy classed professors of mathematics as naval officers, complete with uniform, Newcomb worked up to rear admiral. A great joiner, he belonged to no less than forty-five foreign societies. His main contribution to science consisted of astronomical computations more accurate than any before. He also wrote a delightful autobiography; but he was so wrapped up in his own affairs that he got two-thirds through the book before he even mentioned his wife.

James Joseph Sylvester (1814–97) was a colorful character who came from England in 1841 to teach at the University of Virginia. The campus at this time was overrun with arrogant young Southern gentlemen who not only brought their own slaves to serve them in college but also carried pistols with which to shoot people who offended them. Just before Sylvester arrived, one student had killed a professor on the campus but was acquitted because the victim was only a foreigner. Hating slavery, Sylvester got into an argument about it with a student, who challenged him to a duel.

Seeing no reason to serve as a target, Sylvester demanded that the authorities discipline the youth. When the authorities refused to do so, Sylvester went back to England and accepted a professorship at the Royal Military Academy.

In 1876, Sylvester returned to the United States for seven busy years at Johns Hopkins University, where he founded the *American Journal of Mathematics*. Although his main mathematical work was in the field of invariants, he was also a classical scholar, a poet, and a musician.

Really big strides in mathematics were made in America following Sylvester's stay at Johns Hopkins. By the end of the nineteenth century, American mathematicians who had made impressive contributions to the science of mathematics became too numerous to list.

The American colonies produced one first-class physicist, Benjamin Thompson (1753–1814). Unfortunately, Thompson's scientific career flowered in Europe; for, in the American Revolution, Thompson took the British side.

Beginning as a merchant's apprentice in Salem, Massachusetts, the tall, handsome, hawk-nosed Thompson taught school in Concord (formerly Rumford), New Hampshire, married a rich widow, and became intimate with Loyalist circles in the early 1770s. When the Revolution began, one of the revolutionary committees accused him of spying for the British and put him in jail for two weeks. Long afterward, when some of Thompson's letters were found in the British government's files, it turned out that the committee was right; Thompson *had* been spying.

Released, Thompson fled to England and served as a British army officer against the rebels. After the war, he retired from the army and went to Austria to seek his fortune. An unscrupulous adventurer as well as a brilliant scientist, Thompson fell in with the Elector of Bavaria, whom he charmed into offering him a job. Soon Thompson became Lord High Everything of Bavaria: Minister of War, Minister of Police, lieutenant general, Chamberlain of the Court, State Councilor, and—to top it off—Count Rumford of the Holy Roman Empire. He reformed the army, built a big public park in Munich, and sent all the beggars to a workhouse where they were taught trades and made to be clean and industrious whether they wanted to be clean and industrious or not.

Thompson's greatest discovery concerned the nature of heat. Up to this time, scientists had thought of heat as a weightless, invisible fluid, which they called "caloric." By experiments in Bavaria with the boring of cannon, Thompson developed the theory that heat was simply the motion of the particles of which the hot substance was made.

Perhaps we ought to say a word about scientific theories. A theory is an *explanation* for a set of natural facts, which ties them together and makes it possible to discover more such facts. The more understandable the theory makes these facts, and the more new facts it helps us to discover, the more useful it is. No theory is ever the last word on any subject, because new facts are always turning up, and more accurate measurements are being made. These new findings make it necessary to modify the older theories and sometimes—though not very often—to discard them altogether.

People sometimes ask: has this or that theory been proved? We cannot *prove* a theory in the same sense as we prove an example in mathematics, where the proof consists of showing that one gets out of the equation exactly what he has put into it. All we can do is to gather all the evidence we can and see whether it supports the theory. When the evidence is overwhelming, as it is for the theory of evolution or the theory that the earth is round, we can take the theory, for practical purposes, as an established fact.

Thompson's work shows how overwhelming evidence for a theory is obtained. For his experiments with heat, Thompson took one of the six-pounder guns being bored in the Elector's gun factory. (A "six-pounder" was a gun that threw a six-pound cannon ball.) Thompson immersed the cannon in a barrel of water and set the horses to turning the gun against the tool. Presently, to the spectators' astonishment, the water boiled.

Further tests showed that the water would boil as long as the boring continued. The division of the metal into smaller pieces was not the source of the heat, because the water boiled even when the cannon was turned against a dull tool that failed to cut. The heat could not come from the air (as some believers in "caloric" thought) because the gun was under water. In his report to the Royal Society, Thompson concluded it was "impossible to form any distinct idea of anything, capable of being excited and communicated, in the manner the heat was excited and communicated in these experiments, except it be MOTION." [2]

Rumford (as Thompson was known from then on) made many other discoveries, mostly having to do with heat. He made the first attempt to measure the quantity of heat equivalent to a measured amount of mechanical work; discovered infrared radiation, such as is given off by any warm body; discovered convection currents in heated liquids; and measured the heat given off by the burning of various fuels. He invented many household gadgets, including the coffee percolator, and founded the science of nutrition.

Returning to England from Bavaria, Rumford organized the Royal Institution to present lectures on science to the public. As a firm believer in benevolent despotism, he organized relief for the poor. But he quarreled with his fellow scientists, who disliked his arrogance, and spent his last years in retirement in France as a lonely, crusty old crank, practicing queer fads in clothes and diet.

The sciences of physics and chemistry finally flowered in America during the late nineteenth and early twentieth centuries. Aside from Benjamin Thompson, the outstanding early figure in physics and chemistry was Joseph Henry (1797–1878). A tall, craggy-looking, mild-mannered upstate New Yorker, Henry prepared himself for a scientific career in the only way then open: by studying medicine. For several years he taught at the Albany Academy while experimenting with the electromagnet, a device just invented by William Sturgeon in England.

Sturgeon had varnished a horseshoe-shaped iron bar and wound a bare wire around it to carry the electric current. This system worked well enough up to a point. If, however, one tried to wind too many coils around the bar, the turns would touch one another. Then the current would leap from one turn to the next, shortening its path and reducing the power of the magnet.

Henry was pondering this problem at home in Albany when he startled his friends by suddenly slapping the table and crying: "I have it!" [3] What he had was the idea of insulating the wire itself. Using silk ribbons from his wife's petticoat, he wound 400 turns of wire around his iron core, then 400 more turns on top of the first lot of wire, and was delighted to find that his electromagnet would lift twenty-eight pounds. Further experiments produced electromagnets that lifted the unheard-of weight of 750 pounds. Henry also built the first electro-magnet to be put to commercial use—a magnet for extracting iron from ground-up ore at the Penfield Iron Works.

In 1831, Henry built an electromagnetic telegraph, which rang a small office bell at the end of a pair of wires. The princi-ple was the same as that of the modern electric doorbell, which Henry may be said to have invented. He also built the world's first electric motor. This consisted of a bar electromagnet pivoted at its center like a walking beam. The bar rocked back and forth at a rate of more than one wobble per second, but it did no useful work. Like Heron's steam engine two thousand years earlier, it merely demonstrated a principle. Henry called his motor a philosophic toy and hoped that a practical use would someday be found for it!

Rotary electric motors were invented a few years later, around 1834, by several people at the same time in the United States, Great Britain, and in Russia. They were of little use, however, because the only source of electric current then known was the battery cell; and the batteries were very heavy and costly in proportion to the power they gave. Not until fifty years later, when the electric generator was invented, did the electric motor become practical.

In 1832, Henry became a professor at Princeton University, where he taught and experimented for fourteen years. During this period he and his friend Michael Faraday (1791–1867) in England, working independently, discovered the generator effect, the principle of electromagnetic induction, and the prin-ciple of self-induction. The generator effect is this: if you move a bar magnet through a wire coil, a current is made to flow in

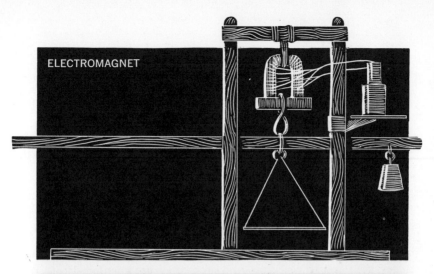

ELECTROMAGNET

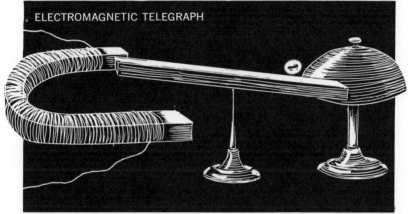

ELECTROMAGNETIC TELEGRAPH

HENRY'S ELECTRIC MOTOR

the coil. Henry discovered this effect a little sooner than Faraday; but, since Faraday published it and so gave it to the world first, he is usually given the credit for the discovery. The generator, the transformer, and the spark coil all depend upon these discoveries made by Henry and Faraday at this time.

In 1836, Henry met Samuel Finley Breese Morse (1791–1872), a lean, sharp-faced man with fluffy gray hair. Morse, the leading American portrait painter of his time, was one of many inventors who were experimenting with the idea of sending messages over wires by electricity. Having no scientific training but plenty of energy, Morse sought advice from men like Henry and Benjamin Silliman, who gave suggestions freely without asking anything in return.

To support himself when the going was rough, Morse brought the process of photography, newly invented by Louis J. M. Daguerre (1789–1851) of France, to the United States and became the nation's first commercial photographer. By combining ideas from many sources, associating himself with several other men, like Leonard Gale, who were better technicians than he, staging demonstrations in Washington, and tireless lobbying, Morse finally got a subsidy of $30,000 from Congress to build his telegraph lines. Much of the money was wasted because Morse insisted on laying an underground cable. When the cable proved defective, Morse and his partners learned what they should have found out sooner: that European telegraph inventors had satisfactory results with a bare wire strung on poles.

So wires were strung on poles from Washington to Baltimore. At the official opening of the line in 1844, Annie Ellsworth, daughter of the Commissioner of Patents, picked for the first message a sentence from the Bible: "What hath God wrought?" The message traveled clearly over the wires; and Morse was on his way to becoming a telegraph magnate.

Actually, Morse's telegraph was not the first of its kind in use. Charles Wheatstone (1802–75), a shy young British physicist and another of Henry's friends, had developed a telegraph system of his own. It had five dials with rotating hands. This system was installed on a British railway and was used soon afterward to catch a murderer. But Morse's system proved so much more practical that it took the place of all other systems.

Truth to tell, Morse was not so much an inventor as a promoter of inventions and a manager of inventors. His success depended less upon his inventions in telegraphy, which did not amount to very much, than upon his drive, his shrewdness, and the indomitable determination with which he pursued his goal even when he was almost reduced to starvation. The main inventions underlying Morse's telegraph system were those of Joseph Henry and Morse's associate Leonard Gale. But despite his virtues, Morse was a vain and touchy man, who later tried to deny that he had received any help from Henry.

In the 1830s, the United States received a bequest of £104,-960 from James Smithson (1765–1829), a British scientist, "to found at Washington, under the name of the Smithsonian Institution, an establishment for the increase and diffusion of knowledge among men." Smithson was a physicist, a mineralogist, and the illegitimate son of a duke. He nursed a grudge against his own country because its social leaders had not accepted him, in spite of his money and his solid scientific standing.

After a ten-year wrangle, Congress created the Institution under a Board of Regents. The Board chose Joseph Henry as the first secretary. Carefully, thriftily, Henry built up the Institution to be the nation's leading scientific center. He launched expeditions, made researches, and issued publications. He was forced against his will to accept an ornate new building of brown fieldstone, ornamented with useless medieval towers, which still stands in Washington, D.C.

As far as his paper-work duties allowed, Henry continued his own researches into metallurgy, acoustics, liquid measurements, and foghorns. He helped to found the American Association for the Advancement of Science, set up in imitation of an older British organization. During the Civil War, the Smithsonian served as the Union's office of research and development; it promoted, for instance, the use of balloons for observation. President Lincoln sought refuge from the cares of office and the sharp tongue of his wife by going to the Smithsonian at night to help Henry. He held apparatus for Henry and took part in experiments involving signaling with lanterns from the towers of the Institution building.

In the exact sciences, perhaps the greatest intellectual giant the United States has ever produced was Josiah Willard Gibbs (1839–1903). Gibbs—a slight man with a high, querulous voice and a long, horsy face, later disguised somewhat by a short beard—lived in New Haven. He studied for his advanced degrees in Germany, as did many young American scientists during the years 1850 to 1914. For Germany then led the world in scientific achievement.

Returning from his travels, Gibbs settled down as a professor at Yale. He never married. He spent all his waking hours in thought; and he thought deeply.

Single-handed, Gibbs laid the foundations of the science of physical chemistry. He also greatly advanced the science of thermodynamics, which deals with the behavior of heat, by working out the underlying theories and then writing treatises with titles like *On the Equilibrium of Heterogeneous Substances*.

These works are as forbidding as their titles, consisting mainly of hundreds of mathematical equations. They deal with the relationships that exist among heat, energy, and temperature, in such chemical and physical processes as burning, boiling, and melting. When the greatest physicist of the century, the Scotsman James Clerk Maxwell, died in 1879, a fellow scientist said: "Only one man lived who could understand Gibbs's papers. That was Maxwell, and now he is dead." [5]

Actually, Gibbs's work, although difficult, was not quite so mysterious as all that. It can be understood, but it takes a lot of hard study. One of his most important discoveries was the phase rule, which may be stated thus: the number of degrees of freedom of a polyphase system in equilibrium equals $n + 2 - r$, where n is the number of components and r the number of phases in the system.

Does that sound obscure? It is, and it would take a whole chapter to explain it. Nevertheless, Gibbs's principles enabled Fritz Haber (1868–1934) in 1913 to work out a method of artificially forcing the nitrogen in the air into chemical compounds. This discovery provided the German Empire with explosives and fertilizers for the First World War and enabled that nation to fight most of the world for four years without importing materials from beyond its battle lines.

Thus, by the end of the nineteenth century, America at last was able to make contributions to pure science along with the leading nations of Europe. The American people began to recognize the need for trained men in the field of pure science. They saw that increased knowledge of the pure sciences was necessary if they hoped to continue to surge forward in the applied sciences and to improve the many factory-made articles that were making life in America enviable to people the world over.

Therefore, governmental bureaus to foster science came into being and multiplied. In 1893, groups of scientists founded the first two specialized American scientific journals—the *Physical Review* and the *Astrophysical Journal*—so that they could keep abreast of the new developments in their fields. Columbia University awarded a degree to its first graduate student in physics: Robert Andrews Millikan (1868–1953), who became one of the world's leading physicists.

In 1899, the American Physical Society was founded, with Henry Augustus Rowland (1848–1901) of John Hopkins University as its first president. Rowland, a tall, hatchet-faced man, who looked a little like an angry stork, was a physicist of considerable achievements. He improved the diffraction grating, an instrument extremely useful in astronomy. When the Niagara Power and Construction Company asked his advice about harnessing Niagara Falls, he wisely advised them to design their plant to generate alternating, instead of direct, current. Then, when he presented his bill, they balked at paying.

Rowland sued the firm. When asked during the trial:

"Who, in your opinion, is the greatest physicist in the United States today?"

Rowland replied calmly: "I am."

Later, when his friends joshed him about his reply, he looked at them in amazement and said that, after all, he had been under oath to tell the exact truth, hadn't he? [6]

VIII · THE SKY ABOVE

Astronomy plays a leading part in the story of American science, because this nation alone had both the wealth to build large observatories and high mountains in desert regions where the night skies are clear.

In spite of the pioneering of men like Winthrop and Rittenhouse, American astronomy was slow in starting. In 1832, a British astronomer reported that there was not one public observatory in the United States. In a young nation devoted to practical development, the study of the stars seemed like a waste of time and money.

Observatories began to appear in the United States in the 1830s and 40s. Then, in the 1860s, a New York lawyer, Lewis M. Rutherfurd (1816–92), made the most important advance in astronomy since the telescope: he invented the astronomical photograph. From that time on, American astronomy progressed by rapid strides.

Much of this progress was the work of Alvan Clark (1804–87) and his sons. One of these sons, as a student at Andover, became interested in astronomy. One day in 1844, his father, who was a successful portrait painter, asked the young man what he was doing. Finishing the reflector of a telescope, replied the son.

Clark became so interested in telescopes that he gave up

painting for a new career as a maker of telescope mirrors and lenses. Five times he was called upon to make refractor lenses larger than any then in existence. With one of these, the 26-inch telescope ordered for the Naval Observatory, Professor Asaph Hall (1829–1907) in 1877 discovered the two satellites of Mars, Deimos and Phobos.

Beginning in the 1870s, a series of generous gifts from rich men made possible the building of several great American observatories. James Lick (1796–1876), a Pennsylvanian who had made his fortune in real-estate speculation in San Francisco, founded the Lick Observatory on Mount Hamilton, California, and gave it a 36-inch refracting telescope made by the Clarks.

A refracting telescope, or refractor, is a telescope of the type invented by three Dutchmen around 1609, in which light passes through a series of lenses mounted in a tube or barrel and an image appears, enlarged, at the lower end. In a 36-inch telescope, the main lens is 36 inches in diameter, while the tube may be of various lengths according to the maker's design.

In 1668, Isaac Newton invented another type, the reflecting telescope. In a reflector, light passes through an open tube or framework to strike a concave mirror at the lower end. It is then reflected back to a set of mirrors and lenses inside the tube, and thence directed to one side, where the observer or the camera stands. Reflectors are commonly used for large instruments, not only because a refractor wastes light by reflecting some of it back as it passes through the lenses, but also because very large lenses sag enough from their own weight to distort the images of heavenly bodies. The mirror of a reflector, on the other hand, can be braced from behind to prevent this sag.

In the 1880s, the University of Southern California ordered a 40-inch refractor from the son of Alvan Clark, Alvan G. Clark (1832–97), who was running the telescope shop after his fa-

LICK OBSERVATORY—36" REFRACTOR TELESCOPE

ther's death. The younger Clark bought a pair of glass disks from a French optical firm. When an expected gift failed to arrive, the university canceled its order, leaving Clark $20,000 out of pocket.

Clark complained of this treatment at a scientific meeting. He was overheard by George Ellery Hale (1868–1938), a young astronomer who was then becoming known as an authority on the sun. Hale had invented an instrument, the spectroheliograph, which made it possible to photograph different parts of the sun's atmosphere, showing details that were lost in the glare in ordinary photography.

On his return to Chicago, Hale urged the president of the University of Chicago to buy Clark's disks for an observatory, provided that Hale could raise the money. Hale chose as his prospective donor Charles T. Yerkes (1837–1905), a streetcar magnate who had made a vast fortune by dishonest means. To square himself with the people of Chicago, Yerkes gave the money for an observatory to be built in Wisconsin.

Later, Hale set up a solar observatory on Mount Wilson in Southern California. This has grown into one of the largest observatories in the world. John D. Hooker (1838–1911), a Los Angeles businessman, in 1906 gave Hale money for the world's biggest telescope: a 100-inch reflector. But it took eleven years and an additional half-million dollars from Andrew Carnegie (1835–1919), the philanthropic steel magnate, to complete the instrument and its mounting.

Soon, with the help of Albert A. Michelson's interferometer —an instrument that breaks a beam of light into two and then reunites them for delicate measurements—the Hooker telescope gave the first accurate measurement of the diameter of a star, the red giant Betelgeuse, in the constellation Orion, which measures 350 million miles. Betelgeuse is so vast that, if the sun were at its center and the planets of the solar system circling around the sun as they do now, the earth's orbit would lie inside the star!

Percival Lowell (1855–1916), of a famous Bostonian family, was another leading American astronomer of the early twentieth century. After distinguishing himself at Harvard, Lowell engaged in business in Boston, traveled in the Orient, wrote books about Japan and Korea, held a diplomatic post, and became a brilliant writer and lecturer.

In 1877, the Italian astronomer Giovanni Schiaparelli (1835–1910), looking through his telescope at Mars, saw—or thought he saw—a number of fine lines crisscrossing the surface of the planet. Schiaparelli drew those lines on maps of Mars, which he published during the next decade. He called the lines *canali*, or "channels." Optimists translated this word as "canals" and inferred that these canals were made by intelligent, living beings.

In the early 1890s, Lowell heard that Schiaparelli's eyesight had given out. Having long been fascinated by astronomy, Lowell decided to carry on the study of Mars where Schiaparelli had left off. On a mesa in Arizona, which has a much better climate for astronomers than Boston, Lowell built an observatory at his own expense. This observatory had three telescopes, headed by a 40-inch reflector. There Lowell and his assistants pursued many astronomical researches. The discovery of the planet Pluto by Clyde Tombaugh in 1930 resulted from the calculations of Lowell and others.

Lowell's main enthusiasm remained planetary research, especially the study of Mars. With less caution than Schiaparelli had shown, he argued in his books that the *canali* were in fact canals made by intelligent beings. The Martians, said Lowell, had built the canals to bring in water from the polar regions of their dried-up planet. The theory became vastly popular. Edgar Rice Burroughs (1875–1950), Tarzan's creator, wrote a whole series of novels about the swashbuckling adventures of his hero John Carter on a Mars built according to Lowell's theory.

From what has been learned of Mars in recent years, however, it looks as though Lowell's theory was just a wrong guess. For one thing, the *canali* would have to be at least fifty miles wide to be seen from the earth at all. Hence they could hardly be canals in the usual sense, although there might conceivably be strips of plant life bordering these canals. Elihu Thomson argued that the lines were the tracks of migrating herds of animals. Others have thought they were cracks in the planet's crust caused by earthquakes, or sand-dune patterns made by the prevailing winds, or streaks of ash from erupting volcanoes, or mere illusions caused by eyestrain.

Some of these questions, however, were settled by the photographs and measurements made on July 14 and 15, 1965, by the American spacecraft Mariner IV. These failed to show any *canali,* but they did indicate that the Martian atmosphere is— and probably always has been—so near to a vacuum that it is unlikely ever to have supported native life of any kind. The surface of the planet is pocked by craters, probably, like those of the moon, caused by large meteors striking the surface billions of years ago, before the planet had swept most of such cosmic rubbish out of its orbit. It is not even likely that this cold, dry, dead, and almost airless planet has earthquakes, since it is probably solid rock all the way through, instead of having a liquid iron core like that of the earth.

One of the greatest triumphs of the Mount Wilson 100-inch telescope was measuring the size of the universe. For many centuries astronomers had wondered how far away each star might be. Long ago, they sought to answer this question by measuring the *parallax* of a star—that is, its apparent movement back and forth, with relation to other stars, as the earth goes round the sun. The trouble is that the nearest star is so far away, and hence this movement is so small, that it is like measuring the diameter of a pinhead at a distance of two miles.

In 1838, two European astronomers, Friedrich W. Bessel (1784–1846) and Thomas Henderson (1798–1844), made the first fairly accurate measurements of the universe. They found that the star Alpha Centauri was 4.3 light-years away and that the star 61 Cygni was 11.1 light-years away. (A light-year is the distance light travels in a year, or about 6,000,000,000,000 miles).

Around 1910, Miss Henrietta S. Leavitt of Harvard University (1868–1921) discovered another tape measure for measuring the distances to the various stars. There is a kind of star called a Cepheid variable, which pulsates, varying from bright to dim and back again in a cycle that may be as short as a few hours or as long as eight days. Studying the Cepheids of the Lesser Magellanic Cloud—a cluster of stars visible from the Southern Hemisphere of the earth—Miss Leavitt found that the larger the Cepheid, the longer its period. As these particular Cepheids were all in one star cluster, they were approximately the same distance from the earth. Therefore, their differences in brightness were differences in the stars themselves and not differences in distance.

Beginning in 1917, Harlow Shapley, at the Mount Wilson Observatory, discovered Cepheids in other star clusters. He suggested that, if the distance of the nearest cepheids could be measured directly by parallax, and their size calculated from the length of their brightness cycles, it would be a simple calculation to determine the distances of other star clusters by the brightness of their Cepheids.

In the 1920s, the 100-inch telescope on Mount Wilson revealed to the astronomer Edwin Powell Hubble (1889–1953) the nature of spiral nebulae. Astronomers had long argued about these fuzzy, pinwheel-shaped objects, the two or three brightest of which can barely be seen by the naked eye.

Hubble made photographs of these nebulae, showing stars embedded in them. He proved that nebulae were galaxies similar to the one that includes our own sun and all the stars that we can see with our naked eyes. He also calculated how far away these galaxies are from our earth.

In the 1920s, Hubble and his assistant Milton L. Humason

measured, not only the distances of the extragalactic nebulae (as the spiral groups or swarms of millions of stars are called) but also the speed at which they are moving toward or away from the earth. They found that most of the galaxies are flying away from one another, and that the more distant ones flee the fastest. This means that the universe is expanding or exploding. The idea of an ever-expanding universe set off a lively scientific argument (which still rages) about the origin and history of the universe.

After the First World War, a nervous disorder forced George Ellery Hale to leave astronomical research. He continued, however, to organize and administer astronomical projects. In the 1920s, he thought the time had come to start a telescope even larger than the 100-inch Hooker reflector. A 300-incher, he found, could be made but not moved. Therefore, Hale proposed a telescope 200 inches (16 feet, 8 inches) in diameter. He went to see Wickcliffe Rose, head of the Rockefeller General Education Board, a group which donated the Rockefeller millions to worthy projects. Rose asked how much the monster would cost.

"Six million dollars," said Hale.

"Doctor Hale," said Rose calmly, "I think you can count on Rockefeller support for the entire sum."

"*For the whole thing?*"

"For the whole thing."

The usually dignified Hale shouted his pet quotation from Jules Verne's novel, *A Journey to the Moon:* "A frightful cry was heard, and the unfortunate man disappeared into the telescope!" [1]

California Institute of Technology set up a council to build the telescope. First, they ordered a mirror of quartz. Quartz (silica or crystal) stretches and shrinks very little with changes in temperature; but it is hard to handle because it melts only at the scorching temperature of 2600 degrees Fahrenheit. The General Electric Company's Elihu Thomson (1853–1937) undertook to make the reflector of quartz in his laboratory at Lynn, Massachusetts. Although he and his engineers overcame enormous difficulties, their disk cracked as it cooled.

The council then ordered a disk of pyrex glass from the Corning Glass Works in upstate New York. This company had a long series of troubles. Time and again, when molten glass was poured into the mold, parts of the mold broke loose and bobbed to the top of the flood. When these difficulties were overcome, the disk was threatened by an earthquake and two floods of the Chemung River. The second of these occurred just as the disk was being mounted on a truck trailer to be hauled out of the factory.

After a narrow escape from being washed away, the enormous mirror was put on a special railroad car, with a padded well to hold it. It arrived in Pasadena, California, in 1936. Although the job of grinding was interrupted by the Second World War, the mirror was finally finished and, in November, 1947, trucked up Mount Palomar during a snowstorm.

Even after the mirror had been clamped into its enormous mounting, it took a year of adjustment before the new telescope was ready to begin work. Soon, however, important discoveries were reported from Palomar. Walter Baade (1893–1960), a German astronomer, used it to discover that stars fall into two classes. Stars of "Population I" occur mostly in the spiral arms of the galaxies. Stars of "Population II," whose members are mostly older, are found mainly in the galactic centers.

As a result of this discovery, it was learned that the neighboring galaxies are about twice as large and twice as far away as had been thought. It also followed that the universe has been expanding at least twice as long as had been supposed. Guesses concerning the time that the galaxies have been flying apart now range from five billion to fourteen billion years.

Telescopes gather, focus, and record the visible light from the heavenly bodies. These bodies, however, also give out radiations of many other wave lengths, longer and shorter than those of light. Around 1930, Karl Jansky (1905–50) of the Bell Telephone Laboratories discovered radio waves coming from the sun. Later it was learned that many astronomical objects give out these radiations. After the Second World War, a number of radiotelescopes, special receivers for such waves, were built in Great Britain, Australia, and the United States. They look like enormous radar antennae.

When radiotelescopes were set to watch the skies, astronomers soon discovered that some of the sources of radio waves were single stars or whole galaxies that could be seen in light telescopes. Other sources did not appear upon the photographic plates of light telescopes at all. One fascinating class of objects discovered by this means is that of the quasi-stellar objects, or "quasars" for short. American, British, and Australian astronomers discovered them in recent years. ("Quasi" is a Latin word meaning "as if.")

As detected by radiotelescopes, quasars turned out to be what looked on the plates of light telescopes like rather dim stars. When astronomers studied the spectra of these stars, however, they found they were the most distant visible objects in the universe—millions of light-years away. At the same time, the radiations from these objects showed that they were putting out energy equal to a trillion suns, or dozens of ordinary galaxies. Astronomers are still wondering and speculating about the conditions that could cause the liberation of such inconceivable quantities of energy for millions of years at a stretch.

Meanwhile, the shorter ultraviolet radiations, which the atmosphere almost entirely stops from reaching the surface of the earth, have been studied by telescopes carried into the upper atmosphere by rockets and balloons.

By the middle of the nineteenth century, geologists had collected so much evidence about the processes that have made the surface of the earth what it is today that many of them had come to doubt that the earth had been created all at once, as the Bible says, about six thousand years ago. They became convinced, instead, that it had come to be through natural processes that had been at work for a much longer time.

In the late eighteenth century, the German philosopher Immanuel Kant (1724–1804) and the French astronomer Pierre Simon, Marquis de Laplace (1749–1827), thought that the entire solar system grew out of a whirling cloud of gas that condensed and drew together into separate bodies under the influence of gravity. Another Frenchman, Count Buffon, thought that the planets had condensed from matter that splashed out of the sun when another heavenly body struck it.

The work of nineteenth-century astronomers and mathematicians cast doubt upon all these theories. For instance, collisions between stars must be so rare as to be negligible, because stars are enormously far apart in proportion to their size. However, a modified version of Buffon's theory was brought out in 1900 by two Americans, the geologist Thomas C. Chamberlin (1843–1928) and the physicist Forest Ray Moulton (1872–1952).

As direct collison seemed unlikely, Chamberlin and Moulton supposed that the sun had merely passed close to another star. The pull of gravity between the two had caused bulges on each star—one toward the other star and one on the side away from it, like the tides raised on earth by the moon. This pull had drawn tidal bulges out into long streamers. These streamers broke up and condensed to form planets. A similar theory was advanced by Sir James H. Jeans (1877–1946) and H. Jeffries in England. Later calculations showed that this theory would not work either, because the gases pulled out of the sun by the near-collision would be too hot to condense and would therefore diffuse through space.

Among the recent theories about the birth of the solar system, those of Karl von Weizsäcker in Germany are highly respected. In the 1940s, Weizsäcker suggested that clouds of gas and dust revolved about each other. One of these clouds blew up, and some of its material condensed to form the planets. But, even today, the question of the birth of our solar system remains unsettled. Perhaps during the next few decades as astronomy marches on, the answer to this riddle will be forthcoming.

IX · THE EARTH AND ITS WATERS

Until the eighteenth century, little was known about the composition of the earth and the way in which its mountains, plains, and seas came to have their present form. Even less was known about the long and dramatic history of plant and animal life during the billions of years that have passed since our earth was born.

Modern scientific geology—the science of the earth—began in Germany two hundred years ago. At that time, Germany was the world's leading mining nation; and its people required a working knowledge of the earth in order to discover the many treasures hidden below the surface. In their search for valuable minerals, they made many unexpected discoveries, and from these discoveries grew several whole new sciences: geology, mineralogy, and paleontology among others. In time, these new sciences utterly revolutionized man's knowledge of the past history of the earth.

The father of modern geology was a German named Abraham Gottlob Werner (1750–1817), who first explained that sedimentary rocks like sandstone had been laid down in layers or *strata*,[1] like the layers of a cake, with the most recent layer on top like the icing of the cake. Werner mistakenly thought that all rocks had been so formed. He was corrected by the Scotsman James Hutton (1726–97), who showed that many rocks were made by the action of volcanoes and that others had cooled from a molten state deep inside the earth. Rocks of the two major kinds came to be known as sedimentary rocks (made from sediment) and igneous rocks (of fiery origin).

In the early nineteenth century, there was a lot of talk among scientists about world-wide catastrophes that had wiped out the life of whole continents and created spectacular features like mountain ranges. Sir Charles Lyell (1797–1875) in England showed that world-wide catastrophes were not necessary to explain the present form of the earth. He showed that mountains, plains, and valleys could have been created by the slow, day-by-day action of wind and water.

At the same time, the Swiss-American naturalist, Jean Louis Rodolphe Agassiz (1807–73) showed that, even if the earth had not suffered any sudden catastrophes, it had undergone great changes. While vacationing in Switzerland in 1836, he listened carefully to the idea of a thoughtful chamois hunter named Perraudin. Perraudin believed that the huge ridges of gravel and long lines of boulders scattered about the Alps had been put there by glaciers.

Agassiz studied the Swiss glaciers and concluded that, during the latest geological epoch, which we call the Pleistocene Period, these glaciers had spread far and wide over Europe. Although his colleagues at first thought him crazy, Agassiz collected such a mass of evidence that at last he convinced them.

In 1846, Agassiz moved to the United States and became a professor at Harvard. He lived in Cambridge in a house full of eagles, snakes, crocodiles, and other wild animals. (Once a bear in the cellar broke its chain, got into a cask of wine, and wandered drunkenly into the midst of a dinner party.)

Agassiz did much to popularize the sciences of geology and biology. A biological laboratory, which he started on the coast of Massachusetts, grew into the famous Woods Hole Marine Biological Laboratory.

Agassiz's son Alexander, like his father, became a noted scientist. In his youth, Alexander Agassiz (1835–1910) served with the Coast Survey, determining the American-Canadian boundary in British Columbia. While rowing about the fog-bound waters of Juan de Fuca Strait, he narrowly escaped from two canoeloads of hostile Indians by sheer oar power. Later, he made a fortune speculating in copper mines and spent it supporting marine expeditions all over the world and fostering biological research at Harvard.

During the latter half of the nineteenth century, when the American West was being opened up, geologists were extremely active there. That vast region not only furnished them with whole trainloads of dinosaur bones and other fossils but also fascinated them with such extraordinary geological phenomena as the Grand Canyon, the Yellowstone Park region, the Great Salt Lake, and Yosemite Valley. Parties of eager geologists even came from Europe to see these American wonders.

The United States Government was not idle, either. It sent many geologists to explore the West in order to learn what regions were suitable for farming, stock raising, and mining. At one time, the government had no less than six geologic surveys in the field at once. Naturally, they duplicated one another's work and competed with one another for governmental funds.

After long argument and agitation, Congress in 1880 abolished four of these surveys and set up a new United States Geological Survey in their place. The second head of this survey was Major J. Wesley Powell (1834–1902), the one-armed conqueror of the Colorado River. Powell (who also kept his job as head of the Bureau of Ethnology in the Smithsonian Institution) held his geologic post from 1881 to 1894. He proved himself a dynamic executive and a shrewd politician.

Powell urged many schemes for which, at the time, he was denounced as an empire-building bureaucrat but for which he is now widely respected. He campaigned for a Federal Department of Science; and the National Science Foundation was created in 1945. He pleaded for the organization of "natural hydrographic regions" to manage water resources; and the Tennessee Valley Authority was established in the 1930s. He suggested damming the mighty Colorado at Boulder Canyon; and this was finally done by the Hoover Dam, finished in 1936.

Powell was also an outstanding scientist. He gave the correct explanation of how mountains are formed by erosion. Perhaps the reader has heard how a piece of low, flat land may be up-lifted and carved by streams and rivers into a range of moun-tains. It is wrong, however, to think of these events as happen-ing one after the other. As Powell pointed out, both actions take place at the same time. While the land slowly rises, ero-sion simultaneously carves it into mountains and valleys. There-fore, by the time the land has finished its upward movement, it has already become rugged and mountainous.

By the middle of the nineteenth century, geologists knew that the earth was no mere six thousand years old, as many had once thought. They realized that the earth had a much longer history, measured in hundreds of thousands—perhaps even in millions—of years. They knew that there had been widespread changes in the distribution of land and water upon the earth, and that the earth's history had been punctuated by at least one great ice age.

They had also begun to grasp the manner in which life had evolved. They realized that there had been a long period when the earth's best-developed inhabitants had been water-living invertebrates, similar to today's crabs and shellfish. This period had been followed by an age of fishes and amphibians; then an age of reptiles, when the dinosaurs flourished; and finally an age of mammals, culminating in the rise of man.

Still, geologists were hazy about the details of this history. They had no way to measure the actual lengths of geologic pe-riods. During the last century, while astronomers have been calculating the age of the universe, geologists have been likewise calculating the age of the earth. Each group of scientists has watched the other's discoveries with keen interest, since the two investigations are closely related. Obviously, the earth can be no older than the universe of which it is a part.

Efforts to measure the age of the earth go back to the work of Jefferson's learned French friend, the Count de Buffon. Buffon assumed that the earth had once been white-hot, like the sun, and that it had cooled to its present state like any other sphere of rock. To test his theory, Buffon ordered to be made a number of balls of various stones and metals. He placed these balls in a wire holder, heated them to white heat, and allowed them to cool. From the time it took these balls to cool, he calculated that a ball the size of the earth would need 74,832 years to attain its present temperature. This estimate of the earth's age, although a worthwhile first step, soon proved far too short.

During the past century, other geologists have tried to estimate the age of the earth by assuming that the oceans began their existence as bodies of fresh water, and by calculating the rate at which streams and rivers have been carrying salt, dissolved out of the rocks, down into the sea. By this method, they estimated the earth's age from 24,000,000 to 100,000,000 years. Others tried to estimate the time required for rivers to lay down the beds of silt that later turned into sedimentary rocks. None of these calculations gave consistent results.

The discovery of radioactivity by Becquerel and the Curies, at the end of the nineteenth century, provided a new method for estimating the age of the earth and explained why Buffon had been so wildly wrong in his attempt to calculate it. Radioactive materials are widespread in the earth's interior; when they break down radioactively, they release heat. A small sample of a radioactive mineral, such as a pound of the uranium ore, pitchblende, gives off very little heat at any one time; but the earth is so large that the total amount of heat released is tremendous. In fact, the heat thus created in the earth's interior replaces the heat that slowly leaks through the earth's surface and is radiated away into space almost as fast as it is lost. Therefore, the rate at which the earth cools is far slower than anything Buffon could have imagined.

Knowledge of radioactivity makes possible a fairly accurate measurement of the earth's age. As the heavy metal uranium disintegrates, each atom of uranium breaks down, little by little, until it becomes an atom of a particular kind of lead. Of any mass of uranium, one half will change into lead in 4,500,-000,000 years. During the next 4,500,000,000 years, half the remainder will turn into lead, and so on. Therefore, careful measurement of the amount of lead in a sample of uranium ore shows just how much time has passed since that piece of ore became a solid.

In the 1920s, the astronomer Henry Norris Russell (1877–1957) in America, and Arthur Holmes in England, calculated the age of ancient uranium-bearing rocks by taking samples of uranium ore from different parts of the world, to see which was the oldest. Obviously, the earth must be at least as old as the oldest minerals in its crust. Many such measurements have been made since then, and the oldest rocks found to date are about four and a half billion years old. Simple forms of life are now thought to have existed on earth for one to three billion years; the oldest fossils of hard-shelled sea creatures go back somewhat over half a billion years.

Because periods so brief as mere thousands of years cannot be measured by the uranium-lead system, other methods have been devised for measuring these shorter periods of time. Baron de Geer of Sweden used the method of counting the layers of silt laid down each year in ancient lake beds by receding glaciers.

Another ingenious measurement of time was devised by Andrew E. Douglass (1867–1962), a Vermonter who became one of Lowell's astronomers in Arizona but who gave up astronomy for local politics. It occurred to Douglass that, since a tree grows faster in wet than in dry years, it should be possible to tell something about the weather of former times by studying the width of the rings in old tree stumps. This he did. He found that, in a given area, all the trees growing at the same time showed the same pattern of growth. Their rate of growth speeded up during a wet year and slowed down during a dry one.

Douglass further discovered that he could compare the growth pattern of a tree of known age with one of unknown age—provided, of course, that the trees were from the same area and overlapped in time. By matching tree rings, like matching the patterns on strips of wallpaper, it was possible to date timbers from the ancient dwellings of the southwestern Indians as far back as 100 B.C.

The most important recent method for measuring the age of the earth is radiocarbon dating, worked out in the 1940s by Willard F. Libby of the University of Chicago. Since this method works on a much shorter time scale than the uranium-lead method—a scale running from about 500 to 20,000 years —the radiocarbon method has been especially useful in dating relics of ancient man. It will, therefore, be discussed in the chapter about archaeology.

The mysteries of the land were not alone in puzzling the men who, in the course of the centuries, wandered over the face of the earth; the seas, which cover three-quarters of the planet, furnished an equally dire assortment of problems and perils. Ancient mariners who set their sails for undiscovered lands did so in fear of storms, whirlpools, unknown monsters of the deep, the wrath of strange gods, and the final hazard of falling off the edge of the earth. Even in the Age of Exploration, when the roundness of the earth had become well known, Columbus's men were thrown into a panic on his first voyage when they found the compass pointing several degrees away from its usual direction—the now well-known phenomenon of magnetic declination.

During the years of the exploration of America, Africa, and

Asia, European sailors noted many things about the winds and weather in various oceans. But the oceans and their ways remained vast and mysterious until an American naval officer, almost single-handed, founded the science of oceanography.

Matthew Fontaine Maury (1806–73) was a studious young man. As an officer in training, he chalked diagrams of spherical trigonometry on cannon balls stacked in their racks and studied these diagrams as he walked the deck of his ship. In the 1850s, he supervised the new Naval Observatory and advised Cyrus W. Field when the latter was planning to lay the first transatlantic cable.

Matthew Maury so loved the sea that he and his assistants dug into old mariners' log books to gather information about wind, wave, and weather in different parts of the oceans. He talked to captains in the merchant marine and published his information in charts to help them manage their sailing ships. He wrote a famous book, *The Physical Geography of the Sea*, which begins with these unforgettable lines of natural poetry:

> There is a river in the ocean. In the severest droughts it never fails, and in the mightiest floods it never overflows. Its banks and its bottom are of cold water, while its current is of warm. The Gulf of Mexico is its fountain, and its mouth is in the Arctic Seas. It is the Gulf Stream. There is in the world no other such majestic flow of waters. Its current is more rapid than the Mississippi or the Amazon, and its volume more than a thousand times greater.[1]

Maury was a Virginian who joined the Confederacy in the Civil War. He spent the war years abroad, trying to buy ships for the rebel government. Later, he worked for the Emperor Maximilian, a puppet prince whom the French installed in Mexico. In 1866, when it was safe to do so, Maury came home to the reunited States and spent the rest of his life as a professor at the Virginia Military Institute.

Since Maury's time, men have learned much about the seas. Divers have studied the shelves that extend out under water from the continents. They have investigated the life forms that swarm in these shallow waters, the wrecks of ancient ships that lie scattered about them, and the deposits of petroleum and other minerals that lie beneath them. Exploration of even deeper waters has also proceeded, step by step. Scientists have lowered waterproof cameras and searchlights to study the bottom; and more recently they have journeyed in special craft to some of the deepest parts of the ocean.

By the early 1930s, diving suits and submarines had taken men down to a depth of about 250 feet. The main problem in reaching great depths is that of pressure. At the surface, the air presses upon all surfaces with a force of 14.7 pounds per square inch. (We do not feel this pressure, because the air within our lungs and dissolved in our body fluids presses outward exactly as hard as outside air presses inward against the surfaces of our bodies. Therefore, the two pressures cancel out.)

A pressure of 14.7 pounds peer square inch, therefore, is called "one atmosphere." For every 33.9 feet that we go down beneath the surface of the water, the pressure rises by one more atmosphere. At a depth of nine times 33.9 feet (305 feet), the total pressure is ten atmospheres, or 1,470 pounds per square inch. This is enough to squash an unprotected human being like a bug.

There are two ways of coping with this pressure. A man must explore the world beneath the waves in some sort of container, such as a diving suit, a diving bell, or a submarine. We can either keep the atmosphere in the container normal and make the container very strong to withstand the pressure from outside; or we can make the container much lighter but raise the pressure inside it to equal that of the water outside. For great depths, the most practical container is a spherical vessel with thick steel walls. In 1889 an Italian, Balsamello, reached a depth of 541 feet in such a sphere.

An American zoölogist, C. William Beebe (1877–1962), made the next advance. A friend of Beebe, Otis Barton, designed and built, to Beebe's specifications, a steel sphere called a "bathysphere," with a hatch and three small round windows of thick quartz. In 1934, the sphere containing Beebe and Barton was lowered by cables from a ship off Bermuda, to a depth of 3,028 feet—over half a mile. As they were being hauled back up, one of the auxiliary cables broke. A terrific shock went through the main cable to the bathysphere. For one horrified moment, Beebe and Barton thought that the main cable had parted and that this was the end for them; but they reached the surface safely.

Fifteen years later, Barton descended to a depth of 4,500 feet in a heavier diving sphere, which was 57.5 inches in diameter and made of 1.75-inch steel. He saw swarms of many strange, luminous sea creatures, including fish, shrimps, octopuses, and jellyfish, living half a mile below the waves.

Meanwhile, an extraordinary Swiss family was developing its own deep-sea craft. In the 1930s, Auguste Piccard, professor of physics in Belgium, his twin brother Jean, and his son Jacques had pioneered in high-altitude balloons. Their flights in pressurized gondolas into the stratosphere touched off international activity in such flights, which culminated in 1935 with the flight to 72,000 feet (just under 14 miles) above the earth by Albert W. Stevens and Orvil A. Anderson, two captains in the U. S. Army Air Corps.

After Piccard had made several such flights, his wife made him promise to make no more. However, he had promised nothing about going down to the bottom of the ocean. After the Second World War, he designed a kind of super-submarine he called a "bathyscaphe." This consisted of a steel sphere of the bathysphere type hung beneath a cigar-shaped tank of light steel, which was filled with gasoline to buoy up the sphere. An electric motor drove the contraption by a small propeller.

In 1953, the 69-year-old Auguste Piccard and his son reached a depth of 10,330 feet (just under two miles) off the

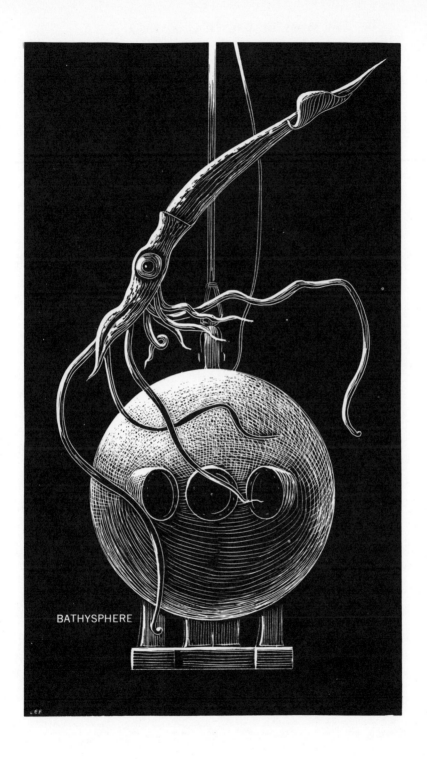

BATHYSPHERE

west coast of Italy. Since then a number of similar craft, manned by Americans, Frenchmen, or a joint Franco-American crew, have explored deeper and deeper, one dive near Puerto Rico reaching a depth of five miles. A number of special deep-water submarines are under construction. Most of them combine an inner sphere of thick steel, to withstand pressure, with an outer hull of thin steel to give the craft a streamlined form.

The latest development in underwater research is a permanent station on the sea bottom, in the form of a steel tank the size of a small house, fitted up with a galley, bunks, and other necessities. The pioneer in this field was a French naval officer, Jacques-Yves Cousteau, who invented the aqualung, the main part of the scuba-diving apparatus. Cousteau's Undersea Research Group set up several such underwater stations in the Mediterranean and the Red Sea.

The U. S. Navy soon followed suit with a "Sealab" off Bermuda and another off the coast of California. The latter, Sealab II, is a permanent installation in the form of a steel cylinder 57 feet long and 12 feet in diameter, standing on steel legs on the sea bottom at a depth of 205 feet. It is manned by a crew of ten men, with a trained porpoise to act as a messenger. In September, 1965, the crew of Sealab II remained under the sea for more than two weeks at a stretch.

These underwater dwellings have hatches in their floors, through which the crews can go in diving suits to explore the undersea world outside. The hatches can be left open, for the air pressure inside the tank is kept as high as that of the water outside. Since the oxygen and nitrogen of the normal atmosphere we breathe become poisonous at such high pressures, the crews must breathe an artificial atmosphere in which extra pressure is furnished by the light, inert gas helium—a method of breathing in the depths suggested by General Electric's Elihu Thomson (1853–1937) in the 1920s.

With such massive attacks from all sides upon the age-old

mysteries of the sea, we can look forward to the time when the oceans will be almost as well known as the land. From this new knowledge, men hope to acquire new sources of food, and of petroleum and other minerals, to support the world's growing population.

X · THE REVOLUTION IN PHYSICS

Physics—the science of matter, motions, force, heat, and radiation—received its name from the Greek natural philosopher Aristotle, over 2,000 years ago. Aristotle derived the word from *physis,* Greek for "nature." But only the most elementary laws of mechanics were known before the seventeenth century. Galileo Galilei, Johannes Kepler, William Gilbert, and Isaac Newton, along with many other scientists previously met in the first chapter of this book, theorized and experimented with the properties of matter during the following centuries. Physics could not become an exact science until these men and their colleagues developed higher mathematics, worked out the experimental or scientific method, and invented precise instruments for making exact quantitative measurements.

Beginning in the last years of the nineteenth century, intensive scientific studies into the nature of matter, energy, and radiation were undertaken in Europe and America. So rapidly did discovery follow discovery that, in the last three-quarters of a century, an entire revolution in physics has taken place. Scientists have determined the speed of light, investigated cosmic rays, and learned how to split the atom and how to use its energy for war and peace.

Today much, but not everything, is known about the physical properties of matter and energy. Scientists have discovered that the line of division between physics and the other physical sciences is not a sharp one. Therefore, several new fields of research have been established, such as physical chemistry (physics plus chemistry); astrophysics (physics plus astronomy); geophysics (physics plus geology); and biophysics (physics plus biology).

The story of man's growing knowledge of physics is a fascinating one, involving many bright, new theories that proved false, many canny deductions that would do credit to Sherlock Holmes, many heartbreaking disappointments and lucky guesses, and not a few dramatic moments. America played a part in this revolution of physics; and, in the past half century, has forged ahead to become the leader in the field.

Men had long argued about radiation. In the seventeenth century, Newton declared that light was made up of little bodies or corpuscles shot out of the sun and other luminous bodies like bullets. His contemporary, the Dutch physicist Christian Huyghens (1629–95), asserted that light was composed of waves, similar in some ways to the waves of sound, or the waves on the surface of the water. Although experiment showed Huyghens to be right, modern physics has discovered that Newton was not altogether wrong, either: light combines the properties of particles and waves.

Nineteenth-century physicists learned that there were many radiations other than those of visible light, all with the same speed. The differences lay in their wave lengths, that is, in the distances between the crest of one wave and the next. The waves of ultraviolet radiation, which causes sunburn, are shorter than those of visible light; those of infrared radiation, which are given off by warm bodies, are longer. Heinrich Hertz (1857–94) discovered the even longer radio waves and Roentgen the even shorter X rays.

In the 1870s, a young American naval officer, Albert Abraham Michelson (1852–1931) measured the speed at which all

these radiations travel in a vacuum. (He used a vacuum because the radiations slow down while passing through matter.)
With a simple but carefully adjusted apparatus of mirrors and
lenses, called an interferometer, Michelson attained a new and
more accurate measurement of the speed of light and found it
to be 186,508 miles a second.

Then Michelson attacked the problem of the ether. When
Huyghens set forth his theory of light waves, the question
arose, waves in what? Trying to answer this question, Huyghens
took the term "ether" from ancient Greek philosophy. He applied this word to an imaginary stuff, filling all space, in which
waves of light were supposed to travel. He thought of the ether
as a kind of thin jelly, which constantly quivered with the
waves sent out from all the many sources of radiation.

However, if the earth swims through the ether like a tadpole
through water, light waves ought to appear to travel at different speeds, depending on whether they go in the same direction as the earth, in the opposite direction, or at right angles to
the earth's course. From the deck of a ship, the speed of waves
appears to vary according to whether the waves are moving in
the same direction as the ship or in the opposite direction.

Michelson, a slight man with piercing eyes, a wispy mustache, and a stiff, unyielding manner, resigned from the Navy
in 1882 to become a professor of physics. He and his colleague
Edward W. Morley (1838–1923) ran a series of experiments
with mirrors to measure the speed of light in two directions,
one along the line of the earth's motion and one at right angles
to it. They found no difference whatever and concluded that
there was no such material as ether surrounding the earth.
Radiations were simply waves in space itself.

That still left the problem of the nature of radiation. Two
physicists, the Irishman George Francis Fitzgerald (1851–
1901) and the Dutchman Hendrik Antoon Lorentz (1853–
1928) suggested a startling theory to account for the behavior
of light; they said that the shape of objects in motion actually

changes at speeds approaching the speed of light, that the objects shrink along their line of motion.

This idea seemed to pose a worse puzzle than the facts it was supposed to explain. A young German physicist, Albert Einstein (1879–1955), who was working in the Swiss patent office, thought and thought about the puzzle. In the early 1900s, Einstein developed his theory of relativity, a theory that connected all the confusing facts into one mathematical whole.

Einstein's theory stated that there is no absolute motion; instead, all motion is relative. Hence there is no need to assume an ether. Rapidly moving bodies not only shrink (or appear to an observer to shrink) but also increase in weight as they near the speed of light. Therefore, no body can exceed this speed, because it would take infinite energy to move an object at such a speed.

Finally, said Einstein, energy and matter are interchangeable, a very little matter being equal to an enormous amount of energy. Experiments have proved that most of the claims of Einstein's theory ($E = MC^2$) are correct.

Meanwhile, man's knowledge of the nature of matter was growing tremendously. Demokritos in ancient Greece had suggested that matter is made of atoms—that is, "unsplittable" particles. The English chemist Robert Boyle in the seventeenth century and John Dalton (1766–1844) in the early nineteenth developed the idea further.

To Dalton, there were a number of elements, such as hydrogen, oxygen, gold, iron, carbon, and sulfur, each made up of atoms of one special kind. Chemical researches supported this idea. The Russian chemist Dmitri Mendelyeev (1834–1907) arranged these elements in order according to the weights of their atoms and showed how they fell into a pattern, with spaces for eighty-odd elements in the pattern. Later discoveries raised the number into the nineties.

In 1897, Sir Joseph J. Thomson (1856–1940), at Cambridge

University in England, learned that an electric current was a stream of small particles with negative electric charges. He found that these small particles, which he called *electrons,* formed parts of atoms. Under some conditions, electrons could be knocked loose from their parent atoms and go streaming off on their own; a stream of such electrons constituted the "electric fluid" of which Franklin and other early electrical experimenters had spoken.

The noted American physicist Robert Andrews Millikan (1868–1953)—a short, handsome, ruddy, strongly built man with a jerky, explosive manner of speaking—got into science in an accidental way: because a job was open. Like other American scientists of his time, he did graduate study in Germany in addition to his work at Columbia University; then in 1896 he became a professor of physics at the University of Chicago.

Millikan undertook to measure the charge on the electron. He floated a tiny droplet of oil in the air between two charged metal plates and made very small changes in its electric charge by pointing a tiny tube of radium salts at it. The change in the droplet's charge was shown by the movement of the droplet toward one of the charged plates. Millikan took the smallest charge of all to be that of a single electron, which he thus defined and measured. Later, Millikan became president of California Institute of Technology and investigated cosmic rays— those mysterious penetrating radiations that continually bombard the earth from outer space.

The next steps in learning how the atom is built were taken in Europe. Ernest Rutherford (1871–1937), a New Zealander working at Cambridge, England, shot charged atoms of the gas helium—the so-called alpha particles—through thin films of gold. He discovered that atoms consisted of a dense nucleus with a positive charge, surrounded by electrons with an equal negative charge, and that ordinarily these charges canceled out.

Just after the First World War, Rutherford found that the

nucleus of an atom contains a number of minute particles which came to be called protons—particles 1,835 times as heavy as electrons, but smaller. Each proton had a positive charge equal to the negative charge of an electron.

During the closing years of the nineteenth century, discoveries in physics came in quick succession. In the 1870s, Sir William Crookes (1832–1919) built a vacuum tube with a pair of electrodes inside it. He learned that, when he applied a voltage to the electrodes, something streamed like a fine wind from the negative to the positive electrode. This something turned out to be a current of electrons.

Then in 1895, a long-bearded, sobersided German professor, Wilhelm K. Roentgen (1845–1923), experimented with a Crookes tube. He found that something was coming out of the tube, right through the glass. Having accidentally left some barium salts near his tube, he saw that, when the voltage in the tube was on but the lights in the laboratory were out, the salts glowed. In this way, he discovered X rays, which were given off when the stream of electrons struck the positive electrodes. X rays proved to be electromagnetic waves, like those of light, except for a much shorter wave length and great penetrating powers. Within weeks of Roentgen's discovery, X rays were being used in surgery to enable the surgeon more surely to find his way inside the body of his patient.

In France, A. Henri Becquerel (1852–1908) set out to find a natural source of X rays. This he did by placing samples of many substances on photographic plates. Then he put keys and other small metallic objects between each sample and its plate so that, if the sample gave off X rays, the plate would be fogged except where the shadow of the key appeared. Becquerel discovered that pitchblende, an ore of the heavy metal uranium, fogged his plates, and so discovered radioactivity.

A pair of physicists in France, Pierre Curie (1859–1906) and his Polish-born wife Marie (1867–1934), took up the further study of uranium. They found several other substances mixed with uranium ore. Two of these were new elements: polonium, which, like uranium, was weakly radioactive, and radium, which, although very rare, was strongly radioactive.

The work of the Curies showed that atoms were not only less solid than had been thought but also less stable. Uranium was always disintegrating, turning by many steps into radium, thence into polonium, and finally into a particular kind of lead. At each step, the radioactive atoms shot out something: sometimes an electron, sometimes the nucleus of a helium atom, sometimes a flash of X rays, and sometimes a combination of all of these.

Marie Curie continued her investigation of radium after Pierre Curie was killed in a street accident in 1906. She became one of two persons ever to be twice a Nobel Prize winner. In 1903, she shared the physics prize with her husband and Becquerel; in 1911, she alone won the chemistry prize.

Since X rays can neither be seen nor felt, early investigators of X rays and radioactivity often suffered crippling or fatal burns from the penetrating radiations. Mme. Curie was one of those whose last years were made agonizing because of radiation sickness.

Meanwhile, other scientists pressed ahead with the study of the atom. In the early 1900s, Niels H. D. Bohr (1885–1962) in Denmark proposed that each atom had a number of electrons whirling around its nucleus, somewhat as planets circle around the sun. These orbits, however, were fixed by the amount of energy in the electrons. If an electron received additional energy, it leaped in a trice from an inner to an outer orbit.

This theory was elaborated further by the Americans Gilbert N. Lewis (1875–1946) in California and by Irving Langmuir (1881–1957) of the General Electric Company in Schenectady. Although Langmuir is less well known than his contemporaries Einstein and Millikan, he was one of the most productive scientists of his time.

Langmuir was a native of Brooklyn, New York: a stocky, sharp-featured man with a brisk, skeptical manner. A scientific jack-of-all-trades, he climbed mountains and flew airplanes for fun, and invented the atomic hydrogen blowtorch, the high-vacuum radio tube, and the gas-filled electric light bulb.

Early light bulbs were evacuated; that is, most of the air in them was pumped out. As a result, when a bulb was dropped, it collapsed with a loud pop and showered the room with glass. Langmuir developed bulbs that were filled with inert gases, which lasted much longer. He also performed a host of experiments in surface chemistry. He learned about the working of thin films, such as occur in a soap bubble or in an oil slick floating on water. In his later years, he worked on chemical rainmaking.

Langmuir's atomic theory was that the nucleus of an atom is surrounded by a series of "shells" or groups of intersecting orbits of electrons. A limited number of electrons can spin about in each shell: two in the innermost shell, eight in the next, eighteen in the next, and so on.

When it turned out that Langmuir's picture of the atom was correct, whole new branches of mathematics had to be developed to explain the behavior of electrons. Hence, in the 1920s, the Austrian Erwin Schrödinger (1887–1961) developed wave mechanics. In 1924, Prince Louis Victor de Broglie of France proposed that the electron, like the photon or light particle, combined the properties of a particle with those of a group of waves.

If electrons have wave properties, why not use them as we use light? thought some scientists. An ordinary light microscope is limited by the fact that it cannot give a clear image when the objects being examined under it are almost as small as the individual light waves. Electron waves, being much shorter, should give a sharper image.

To America belongs most of the credit for the electron microscope. About 1930, Reinhold Rudenberg, a professor at Harvard University, worked out the theory; and the instrument itself was developed by James Hillier and Vladimir Zworykin at the laboratories of the Radio Corporation of America. This microscope shoots a stream of electrons through a thin layer of the substance to be photographed. The electrons are then spread out by electromagnets until they strike a photographic plate. As a result of improvements over the last thirty years, it is now possible to magnify objects half a million times, so that men can see viruses and the larger molecules. Our present-day understanding of genetics is partly due to this very valuable instrument.

Meanwhile, work on the atom continued in the United States. In 1921, William D. Harkins (1873–1951), at the University of Chicago, photographed the tracks of charged particles in a Wilson cloud chamber. This device, invented around 1910 by the Scottish physicist Charles T. R. Wilson (1869–1959), makes it possible to photograph the track of an electrically charged particle through a small chamber. To do this, the experimenter suddenly expands the air in this chamber by means of a piston, so that a fog forms from the sudden cooling, and water condenses in a line of little droplets along the path of the particle.

One of Harkins's pictures showed a helium atom combining with a nitrogen atom to make an atom of fluorine, which broke up at once into one atom each of oxygen and hydrogen, lighter by the weight of one proton than the two original atoms. Obviously, some particle with the weight of a proton had disappeared; and, since it had left no track in the cloud chamber, it must have been a particle with no electric charge. Therefore, Harkins inferred that an uncharged particle existed in the nucleus of at least certain atoms.

In 1932, James Chadwick at Cambridge University, England, discovered that Harkins had been right. In every element except hydrogen, there exists in the nucleus, besides protons, some additional, neutral particles called *neutrons*. Each neutron has the same mass as a proton but no electric charge. In the lighter elements, like lithium and oxygen, the number of neutrons is about the same as that of the protons. But, in heavier elements like lead and uranium, the number of neutrons is much larger than the number of protons.

The best way to learn about the makeup of the atom, scientists found, was to shoot subatomic particles—electrons, protons, neutrons, and the nuclei of helium atoms—at targets made of various elements and study the results. The greater the speed at which these particles could be shot, the more would be learned. In 1929, Ernest Orlando Lawrence (1901–58), professor at the University of California, read a paper by a German physicist who had managed, by giving two electrostatic impulses instead of one, to impart to charged potassium atoms in a vacuum tube twice the energy they would normally get from a given voltage. Lawrence wondered: if the impulse could be doubled, could it not be tripled or multiplied any number of times? The problem was to give the particles a series of impulses a little stronger each time until, like a child being pushed on a swing, the momentum was greatly increased.

Lawrence made a particle-pushing machine of glass and sealing wax. The disk-shaped vacuum chamber was four inches in diameter. Inside were two electrodes, each shaped like half a round cake box and called D-plates because of their shape. Outside the vacuum chamber was a powerful electromagnet, with one pole above the chamber and one below. The D-plates were given electrostatic charges, which alternated at high frequency. Charged particles, turned loose at the center of the machine, were driven first one way and then the other by the charges on the D-plates. At the same time, the magnetic field made them fly in circles—or rather, in a spiral path that wound outward. Back and forth, around and around, faster and faster they went, until they shot out through a window at the outer edge of the vacuum chamber.

With his second model, made of metal, Lawrence found that, with a repeated voltage of only 2,000 volts, he could accelerate his particles to a speed equal to that which a single impulse of 80,000 volts would impart. The device was named the *cyclotron*. Each successive cyclotron was larger and more powerful. By 1940, there were thirty-five cyclotrons in use and another twenty under construction in various nations. One of the latest cyclotrons, at Berkeley, California, has a vacuum chamber 394 feet in diameter and develops several billion "electron volts."

Meanwhile, other physicists have developed particle accelerators ("atom smashers") of other kinds. Some, for instance, shoot their particles in a straight line through a long vacuum tunnel instead of whirling them around and around.

Atoms did not seem too hard to understand so long as there were only three particles involved: the electron (light, with a negative charge), the proton (heavy, with a positive charge), and the neutron (heavy, with no charge). But in the 1920s, a British physicist, Paul A. M. Dirac, predicted that somebody would discover a particle with the size and mass of the electron and a positive instead of negative charge.

In 1932, a young physicist at California Institute of Technology, Carl D. Anderson, took a photograph in a Wilson cloud chamber, which could only be that of the predicted particle, called a positron. So many scientists were working on the atom that, within a few weeks, the same discovery was made by a scientist in Britain, by another in the Soviet Union, and by the husband-and-wife team of the Joliot-Curies in Paris. Jean-Frédéric Joliot had married Mme. Curie's daughter Irène (1897–1956), a physicist like himself, and had changed his name to Joliot-Curie in deference to his wife, a strong-minded woman who later became a fanatical Communist.

In that same year, 1932, the Joliot-Curies created the first artificial radioactivity. They bombarded a boron target with

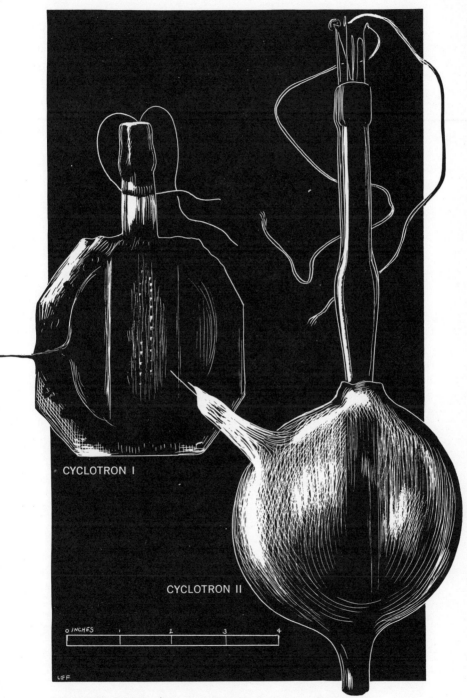

CYCLOTRON I

CYCLOTRON II

0 INCHES 1 2 3 4

LEF

LAWRENCE'S FIRST TWO EXPERIMENTAL CYCLOTRONS

helium nuclei to make radioactive nitrogen. Soon the new atom smashers began turning out artificial radioactive materials for use in medical and biological research. These materials proved of immense value in enlarging our knowledge of biochemistry and genetics.

Before the year 1934, it was known that each radioactive element disintegrated at its own constant rate. Neither heat, magnetic fields, nor anything else seemed to affect this rate of breakdown. In that year, Enrico Fermi (1901–54), an Italian physicist who later became a resident of the United States, found that he could speed up the disintegration of radioactive elements by shooting them with neutrons. Fermi had reasoned that neutrons would make ideal projectiles to shoot at atoms. Electrons were too light to have much effect on the nucleus, while protons were repelled away from the nucleus by the protons already there. (A positive electric charge attracts a negative charge but repels another positive.) But a neutron, having no charge at all, could sail on through the whirling cloud of electrons and smash into the nucleus without hindrance.

Fermi found that when a neutron hit a target atom, it often sank into the nucleus. The result was an atom with the same chemical properties as before but with a greater weight. It was already known that most elements are made up of atoms of two or more kinds, having the same chemical properties but slightly different weights. These varieties of a single element are called its *isotopes*. For example, most atoms of carbon—about 989 out of every thousand, in fact—have an atomic weight of 12; but the remaining eleven atoms out of a thousand have an atomic weight of 13. In addition, there are a very few atoms—less than one in many millions—of carbon of weight 14, which are, moreover, radioactive. This carbon-14 makes possible the radiocarbon dating of ancient relics.

In 1931, Harold C. Urey at Columbia University discovered that even hydrogen has an isotope, "heavy hydrogen" or deuterium, with a nucleus consisting of a proton and a neutron instead of a proton only. One hydrogen atom in 4,000 is an atom of deuterium; and an even scarcer isotope of hydrogen, tritium, exists, which has two neutrons and one proton in its nucleus.

By shooting neutrons at the extremely heavy metal uranium, Fermi hoped to create an element with an atomic weight greater than that of uranium. No such elements were then known, because atoms with very heavy nuclei are unstable. Like radium, they quickly disintegrate into lighter elements.

Fermi thought for a while that he had obtained his Element 93 (uranium being 92 in the periodic table). But two German physicists, Otto Hahn and Fritz Strassmann, repeated Fermi's experiment and discovered that they obtained, not Element 93, but the already-known middleweight element barium.

These discoveries took place in 1938, when Hitler was persecuting the Jews and intellectuals of Germany and was planning to send his mighty armies rolling across the rest of Europe. Many European scientists, in fear of being imprisoned, tortured, or murdered, fled to America. Up to this time, the United States had played a worthy part in the revolution in physics; but, because America promised freedom and security to these homeless European scientists, our nation suddenly leaped to world leadership in the science of physics.

Among those who emigrated from Germany was the sixty-year-old woman physicist Lise Meitner. Her younger cousin O. R. Frisch had already fled to Denmark and gone to work for his father-in-law, Niels Bohr. Here Dr. Meitner presently joined him. As they discussed the recent discoveries in physics, the full implication of the facts dawned upon them. They reasoned thus:

When a neutron strikes an atomic nucleus and makes it disintegrate, the process unleashes a flash of energy in the form of radiation. This energy is enormous as compared with ordinary chemical reactions, although the explosion of a single atom is negligible as far as human beings are concerned.

Now, in all the lighter elements, the numbers of protons and neutrons in the nucleus are about equal. In the heavier elements, however, the number of neutrons is decidedly greater than the number of protons. The heavier the element, then, the greater the excess of neutrons over protons.

When a uranium atom was struck by a neutron, instead of merely coughing out a proton and a neutron or two, it split almost in half, dividing into one atom of barium and one of krypton. Since an atom of uranium has several more neutrons than an atom of barium plus an atom of krypton, the leftover neutrons must have flown off on their own. If the exploding atom were surrounded by enough other atoms of uranium, some of the surrounding atoms would be struck by those flying neutrons and would be exploded in their turn. When one such atom breaks up and its spare neutrons fly out and smash other atoms, and they, in turn, smash others, this is called a *chain reaction*. Under these conditions, the energy released, in proportion to the mass of material, would make ordinary high explosives seem like children's toys.

In the early days of 1939, Bohr journeyed to the United States to attend a conference of physicists. He discussed the new theory with his colleagues—including Einstein and Fermi, who were now American residents and who already knew something of the theory of atomic explosion. A dramatic moment came while Bohr was at the conference: he received a cable sent by Doctors Frisch and Meitner, who stated that they had repeated the Hahn-Strassmann experiment and found that it really worked. Thus it appeared that construction of an atomic bomb might well be possible.

During the following months, many physicists pondered the situation. More than one thought: Germany still has some excellent physicists; what if Hitler develops the atomic bomb? Two scientists, Eugene P. Wigner and Leo Szilard, sought out Albert Einstein at his home on Long Island and talked long and earnestly with him. Horror of Hitler overcame Einstein's lifelong pacifism, and he dictated a historic letter beginning:

F. D. Roosevelt
President of the United States
White House
Washington, D.C.

Sir:

Some recent work by E. Fermi and L. Szilard, which has been communicated to me in manuscript, leads me to expect that the element uranium may be turned into a new and important source of energy in the immediate future. Certain aspects of the situation which has arisen seem to call for watchfulness and, if necessary, quick action on the part of the Administration. I believe therefore it is my duty to bring to your attention the following facts and recommendations.

In the course of the last four months it has been made probable through the work of Joliot in France as well as Fermi and Szilard in America that it may become possible to set up a nuclear chain reaction in a large mass of uranium . . .

Einstein went on to speak of possible new radioactive elements, power sources, and bombs.

The three physicists persuaded a friend—an economist named Alexander Sachs, who was also a friend of President Roosevelt—to deliver the letter to him in person. Just then, on September 1, 1939, Hitler invaded Poland, and the Second World War began. After some delay, Sachs got his appointment with the President. Although Roosevelt knew practically nothing of physics and was overwhelmed by other problems, he grasped the importance of his visitor's message and said:

"Alex, what you are after is to see that the Nazis don't blow us up."

"Precisely."

Roosevelt summoned his secretary. So began the secret building of the nation's first atomic bomb. After some early hesitation and fumbling, the enterprise—given the code name of the Manhattan Engineer District, or the Manhattan Project —grew to colossal size.

When the German government surrendered in May, 1945, the victors found out that the Germans had not even come close to making an atomic bomb. In fact, their leading physicists still believed that the energy developed by atom-splitting could not be harnessed.

In the Pacific, however, the bitter and costly war against Japan continued. Should the frightful new weapon be used to end the Japanese war at one blow? There were strong arguments on both sides of the question. At length, President Truman decided in favor of using the bomb. He knew that the Japanese army had prepared a last-ditch, no-surrender defense of the islands against American invaders, which would probably have cost both nations many more lives than would the use of the bomb. Accordingly, on August 6th, an atomic bomb was dropped on Hiroshima, wiping out most of the city and killing most of its people. When Einstein heard the news, he sadly shook his head, saying:

"*Ach!* The world is not ready for it." [1]

Three days later, Nagasaki suffered the agony of a similar bomb; and Japan surrendered.

After the Second World War, Great Britain, which had cooperated with the United States in the atomic-bomb project, built some bombs of its own. The Soviet Union, having learned some of the secrets of the bomb through its spies, started its own project and exploded its first nuclear bomb in 1949. France and China followed.

After the Second World War, the American, British, and Russian governments began to put nuclear energy to peaceful uses. They built a number of nuclear power plants, in which the chain reaction was carefully controlled, so that its heat generated steam to turn turbines and make electric power. These turbines derive their power, not from ordinary coal or fuel oil, but from the heat of an atomic furnace, or "pile." The first such plant to go into service was the Calder Hall plant in northern England. Since then, a number of others have been built in the United States and in the Soviet Union.

Nuclear engines are also being developed for ships, locomotives, and airplanes. A number of nuclear-powered ships, most of them submarines, have already been put into service. In 1958, the first nuclear-powered submarine, the American *Nautilus,* traveled to the North Pole and back under the ice of the Arctic Ocean. Two years later, another American nuclear-powered submarine, the *Triton,* sailed around the earth in eighty-four days without coming to the surface.

During the twenty-odd years that have passed since the end of the Second World War, study of the atom has continued at a furious pace. Whereas Lawrence's original cyclotron had a chamber the size of a small frying pan, the latest particle accelerators or "atom smashers" cover several acres, weigh thousands of tons, and cost scores of millions of dollars. Now that the arrangements of electrons spinning around the nuclei of atoms are well known, the new accelerators are being used to reveal the structure of the nucleus itself.

As long ago as 1935, a Japanese scientist named Hideki Yukawa suggested that there were particles in the nucleus smaller than protons and neutrons but heavier than electrons. It was later found that such particles did indeed exist and were sometimes shaken out of the nucleus during atomic collisions or disintegration. In fact, so many kinds of particles have been found in the nuclei of atoms that the total number of kinds of subatomic particles has grown from the simple three, known in 1932, to about a hundred.

Many present-day physicists are unhappy about this bewildering complication. They feel that all these subatomic particles may one day turn out to be combinations of a few basic particles. Unraveling this mystery is a task for the next generation of physicists.

The progress of physics in the past seventy years has had an incalculable effect on the lives of all of us. We live in constant danger of atomic destruction and the abrupt ending of our present civilization. At the same time, our government is encouraged by this very danger to cooperate with other governments in order to find peaceful solutions to the world's problems. With luck, the next few years will see the atom harnessed to provide cheap power for the numberless machines that make our civilization possible.

PART THREE
The Biological Sciences

XI · THE SCIENCES OF LIFE

We have seen how man's knowledge of the physical sciences spread across Europe and America during the last half of the eighteenth and throughout the nineteenth centuries. We have seen, too, how this knowledge led to the invention of machinery more intricate than any the world had previously known. We have learned how machines brought a whole new way of life to city and country folk and transformed the face of our farm lands.

Busy creating things, few early American scientists concerned themselves with ideas about the history of man or even about how life come to exist upon our planet. Men in Europe occasionally wondered about the origin of life as long ago as the days of the Greeks, when Xenophanes and Herodotus found sea shells on the mountain tops. But such inquiring minds were few indeed. Then, during the nineteenth century in England, the science of life took a giant step forward: Charles Darwin set forth his theory of evolution by natural selection.

Slow changes in various species of domesticated plants and animals had been observed and encouraged since the beginning of civilization. But it was not until the late eighteenth century that a few thoughtful men studied fossil finds and realized that, over the centuries, there had also been great changes in wild plants and animals. Some began to wonder if there existed in the world of nature a slow, continuous change, like that which farmers brought about among domesticated species by selective breeding. This slow change was called evolution.

Darwin believed that evolution came about by means of natural selection. He argued thus:

All living things compete for food and living space with their own and other kinds. The winners survive to have offspring; the losers die. Now, no two organisms, even of the same species, are exactly alike. They vary. In any species, some individuals are larger, stronger, swifter, keener-eyed, healthier, or more fertile than others. As a result of these qualities, the individuals that possess them have a better chance than the others of surviving and passing these qualities on to their descendants. Thus the fittest members of a species are *selected* by nature, and thus a species changes in the direction that best enables it to survive in its particular surroundings—its environment—pursuing the kind of life to which it is suited by its physical form. When, as often happens, the environment changes, the species has to change with it or become extinct. Thus, foxes are part of a rabbit's environment. To keep from being all eaten by foxes, rabbits have had to evolve longer, stronger legs to enable them to run faster. Then, to keep from starving, the foxes in their turn have had to run faster, so the rabbits have had to run still faster, and so on without end.

It follows that all existing species have changed during the earth's history and that different living species are descended from the same ancestor. In fact, we believe all forms of life now on earth, including man, are descended from one or a few simple, tiny creatures that lived in shallow water over a billion years ago. During the last few geological periods, men evolved from apelike primates. These in turn descended from shrewlike mammals, which evolved from lizard-like reptiles, and so on back through salamanders, fish, and worms to some microscopic blob of primeval living jelly.

At least a hundred men before Darwin conceived the idea of evolution. Some even came close to his explanation of natural selection. Darwin's distinction is that he collected such a mass of evidence and presented it in such an orderly and convincing manner that people with a scientific outlook were forced to accept it. They had to believe it, even if they resented the idea that their forebears once sat on the branch of a tree and scratched their hairy hides.

One of those who laid the foundation of Darwin's theory was Benjamin Franklin. In 1750, Franklin wrote a letter explaining how, when he doubled the number of pigeon boxes nailed to the wall of his house, the number of pigeons at once increased to fill them. He also noted in an article that every species produces far more offspring than are needed to keep up its numbers. If there were no other plants on earth but fennel, for instance, fennel would soon spread over the whole world.

An English clergyman, Thomas Malthus (1766–1834), read Franklin's pamphlet and similar writings by other thinkers. Then Malthus carried the idea further. People, he said, tend to increase until there is not enough food to go around. At that point their numbers stop growing, because they are destroyed by starvation, war, or disease as fast as they are born. If a new country is settled, or if an advance of science makes it possible to raise more crops on the land, people increase for a while. But, sooner or later, population catches up with the food supply. Then they are all back at starvation level, only with more hungry folk than before.

Many people, who thought this a hard-hearted doctrine, denounced Malthus. Nevertheless, his ideas have proved basically correct.

Charles Robert Darwin (1809–82) was a tall, round-faced, good-natured, lazy young Englishman, who studied medicine at the University of Edinburgh. Later, he got a post as naturalist on a British naval vessel, H. M. S. *Beagle*, when it set out on a five-year cruise of exploration and research.

The *Beagle* sailed around the coast of South America and criss-crossed the Pacific Ocean. Darwin suffered horribly from seasickness. He remained in poor health for the rest of his life, perhaps as a result of Chagas's disease. This ailment is trans-mitted by the bite of *Triatoma,* a large, black, squashy South American insect, which attacked Darwin in swarms when he was camping out on the pampas.

After this voyage, Darwin lived quietly in the English coun-tryside on an inheritance, which he built into a tidy fortune by shrewd investments. Here he studied his voluminous notes for twenty years before revealing his theory. He thought and thought about the differences he had seen among animals. These variations seemed to mean something, but Darwin could not quite see what.

Then Malthus's book gave him his clue. If each species in-creases until its homeland can support no more of its kind, and if, in each generation, many individuals perish, then on the average, those best fitted to survive do so. Thus the species evolves or changes, and thus the same species in two different countries will change in different directions and eventually split into two species.

In 1859, Darwin put forth these ideas in a book, *On the Origin of Species by Means of Natural Selection, or the Preser-vation of Favoured Races in the Struggle for Life* (often called simply *The Origin of Species*). This book caused a sensation all over the world. Although some people denounced it because it contradicted the Bible, its reasoning was so strong that evolu-tion soon carried the field in British scientific circles.

In the United States, some scientists, like the botanist Asa Gray (1810–88), were convinced at once. Some, like Louis Agassiz, refused to accept evolution despite all the evidence. Some, like the anthropologist Lewis H. Morgan, secretly agreed with Darwin but dared not admit it for fear of what people would say.

Darwin depended for his arguments on the distribution of animals in the wild state; on the development of animals before birth; on vestigial organs like the human tail; and on the differences that have arisen among breeds of domestic animals. He did not depend very much on what is now the strongest argument for evolution: the evidence of paleontology—the study of the fossilized remains of animals.

In Darwin's time, not enough fossils were known to give a clear picture of how life evolved. Moreover, Europe is a poor country for fossil hunting. Because most of it is covered by trees, grass, and crops, fossils cannot often be seen on the surface. Therefore, it was in America that the science of paleontology reached its greatest development.

Geologists exploring the Great Plains and the deserts of the American West found a much better fossil-hunting ground than anything they had dreamed of. These geologists sent a rich treasure of fossils back east to scientists in various universities, especially to Joseph Leidy (1823–92), a professor of anatomy at the University of Pennsylvania. Leidy studied these fossils and published descriptions of them, thus getting American paleontology off to a good start.

In the late 1860s, the leadership of American paleontology was taken over by two younger men, who entertained the nation with a spectacular and often comical feud. One was Edward Drinker Cope (1840–97) of Philadelphia. Although reared as a Quaker, Cope was one of the most hot-tempered, combative scientists who ever lived. He began exploring the West for fossils in 1868. Three years later, the Cheyennes went on the warpath and killed many whites in the region explored by Cope. But Cope, who refused to carry a gun because of his Quaker principles, amused a committee of visiting Crow Indian chiefs by taking out his false teeth.

The other man was Othniel Charles Marsh (1831–99), a stocky, red-bearded professor at Yale. Where Cope was daring, fiery, and impetuous, Marsh was coldly crafty and grasping. Although Marsh had many solid virtues, many of his colleagues hated him for his unscrupulous selfishness.

Both were determined, aggressive men of great courage and

fortitude. Naturally, once each decided he wanted all the fossils in the West, an explosion was bound to come. When, in 1872, Cope started digging in a part of Wyoming that Marsh considered his private preserve, Marsh put every obstacle in Cope's way. They cheated each other out of fossils, plotted against each other in learned societies and governmental bureaus, and denounced each other to the newspapers for ignorance, incompetence, and dishonesty. The feud died down only when both had spent all their inherited fortunes in outfitting expeditions and outbidding each other for fossils. Cope and Marsh made "dinosaur" a household word in the United States by their many spectacular finds of fossils of dinosaurs, a race of giant reptiles that mysteriously died out about seventy-five million years ago.

Although Cope and Marsh both made many splendid fossil finds, Marsh's proved the more important. His discoveries, more than those of any other man, furnished the final fossil proof of evolution. For instance, according to evolutionary theory, birds are descended from reptiles. Therefore, the ancestors of the present-day birds ought at one stage to have had teeth, like those of their reptilian ancestors. In rocks from the latter part of the Age of Reptiles, Marsh found the fossils of birds with teeth. About the same time, remains of even more lizard-like birds were found in Germany.

Marsh also dug up and arranged in order many fossils of the horse's ancestors. These began with a creature the size of a fox terrier, with four toes on each forefoot and three on each hindfoot. Fossil horses from later periods were larger. Their middle toes grew whereas the side toes dwindled, until they were running on one enormous toe on each foot, as does a modern horse. For the first time, scientists could see a complete series of animals in the same line of descent, changing as age succeeded age.

Even when all this evidence became known, many people balked at the idea of a hairy primate chattering on their family tree. They demanded: Where are the "missing links" between man and ape?

Actually, discovery of such links began in 1848 with the finding in Europe of the skull of a man of the Neanderthal race, which was in some ways subhuman. In the 1890s, the Dutch physician Eugène Dubois found a still better example of an ape man in Java. Throughout the present century, finds of fossil submen have gone on, mostly in Africa and Asia, until now more than a dozen species of such "links" are known. So we have at least a fair idea of what our more recent ancestors looked like.

Such finds are rare, partly because early men were usually too clever to drown in a swamp, where their bones would remain to be fossilized. America played but little part in these discoveries, because man's immediate ancestors lived in the Old World.

Many people in Europe and America opposed the teaching of evolution. In the United States, this opposition reached its height in the 1920s, mainly as a result of agitation by William Jennings Bryan, a politician, reformer, real-estate speculator, former Secretary of State, and thrice-defeated candidate for President. When Bryan was traveling about the nation making speeches against evolution, Henry Fairfield Osborn wrote him, politely inviting him to come to the American Museum of Natural History to see for himself the overwhelming evidence in its favor. Bryan sent a brusque reply, saying he was "too busy." When a reporter asked Osborn about it, Osborn stated that Bryan had refused for fear of having his beliefs shaken. Bryan replied by calling Osborn "a tall professor coming down out of trees to push people not believing in evolution off the sidewalk." [1]

Many conservative ministers, who wished people to believe that everything in the Bible was literally true, joined Bryan's campaign. Tennessee, Arkansas, and Mississippi passed laws against the teaching of evolution. In Tennessee, a young high-school teacher named John Thomas Scopes was tried for break-

TYPES OF FOSSIL MEN

Top: Pithecanthropus, who lived in Java in the middle of the Pleistocene Ice Age; *Middle:* Neanderthal man, who lived in Europe in the latter part of the Pleistocene Ice Age; *Bottom:* Cro-Magnon man, who lived in Europe after Neanderthal man, at the end of the Pleistocene Ice Age.

ing the state's "monkey law." Scopes and his friends had deliberately engineered the case in the hope that a higher court would declare the law unconstitutional.

The "Monkey Trial," at Dayton, Tennessee, in July, 1925, aroused enormous interest. Bryan served as a lawyer for the prosecution, while Scopes had as defenders a number of eminent lawyers, including Clarence Darrow (1857–1938). Judge John T. Raulston tried to run a fair and orderly trial, but this was hard because of the circus atmosphere that sprang up in Dayton. The city swarmed with evangelists and traveling showmen, some of whom displayed tame chimpanzees. Furthermore, the judge was more than a little bewildered himself. In the course of a spectacular trial, Darrow showed that Bryan, although a likable and well-meaning man, knew nothing at all about science. In the end, Scopes was found guilty and fined $100.

However, when the case was appealed, the Supreme Court of Tennessee set aside the verdict, because the judge had committed a legal blunder in levying the fine. At the suggestion of the court, the prosecution killed the case. Scopes, who privately admitted after the trial that he had never had time to teach evolution at all—he had been too busy coaching the football team—became a geologist. Bryan, the crusader for Genesis, died in his sleep a few days after his final struggle to prove mankind above the laws of nature.

In the following decades, the American people grew accustomed to the idea of evolution through books, magazines, and motion pictures. Hence agitation against the teaching of evolution died away in the more advanced parts of the nation. However, Mississippi still has its "monkey laws" (that of Arkansas and Tennessee having recently been declared unconstitutional) and there has lately been agitation for similar laws in Texas and Arizona.

Even after the validity of Darwin's theory of evolution became evident, many scientists were not entirely satisfied with Darwin's explanation of *how* evolution took place. It was all very well to say that the members of a species varied. Once you admitted that, it followed logically enough that the fittest would survive more often than the less fit. But what caused these variations? And, once a variation came into being, would it be passed on unchanged or be lost by blending and modification in later generations?

The first steps towards answering these questions were taken a century ago by a stout, gentle Moravian monk, Johann Gregor Mendel (1822–84). In his monastery garden at Brünn (modern Brno, in Czechoslovakia) from 1857 to 1865, Mendel experimented with the breeding of garden peas. He made a remarkable discovery: When he crossed tall peas with short peas he did not get plants of medium height, as one might expect. The peas of the second generation were all tall.

Then, when Mendel interbred the peas of the second generation, he obtained a lot of mixed offspring. One quarter of the peas of the third generation were tall peas that behaved, when interbred, like any other tall peas of pure ancestry. Another quarter were short peas which behaved like any other short peas.

The remaining peas—half of the peas of the third generation —behaved just like the hybrid, mixed peas of the second generation. That is, when interbred, they gave rise to plants of three different kinds, in the ratio of 1 : 2 : 1. One quarter were true-breeding tall peas, one half were tall but did not breed true, and one quarter were true-breeding short peas.

Other plant breeders had noticed variations of this sort, but Mendel was the first to show that these variations occurred in simple arithmetical proportions. He learned that in peas, such characters as the color and shape of the flowers, seeds, pods, stems, leaves, and other parts followed the same rules of inheritance as the height of the plants. But these parts followed the rules independently, so that a multitude of different combinations of sizes, shapes, and colors could be obtained in the same species of plant.

In 1866, Mendel published his researches in the magazine of the Natural History Society of Brünn and sent copies to various European libraries and to leading scientists. Three years later, he published a second report. But nothing, absolutely nothing, happened. Although Mendel had expressed himself clearly enough, nobody—assuming that some people at least read his articles—understood them, let alone appreciated their importance.

Then Mendel was elected abbot and became embroiled in a furious quarrel over taxes with the government of the Austro-Hungarian Empire. His botanical work dwindled away and ceased. In 1900, after Mendel had been dead for sixteen years, three amazed European biologists rediscovered his reports and hailed Mendel as the founder of *genetics,* the science of heredity. For Mendel had discovered that certain qualities in living things, such as height in peas or the color of their flowers, are passed on either completely or not at all. This is called the *inheritance of unit characters.*

Mendel also found that a quality can be passed on invisibly, so that it bobs up in a later generation. His tall but non-true-breeding peas possessed something that had to do with shortness, which they had inherited from their short parents and could pass on to their offspring. These peas, Mendel reasoned, had inherited both a tallness-character and a shortness-character, one from each parent. However, the tallness-character fixed the plant's height. As he expressed it, tallness was *dominant* over shortness. The hidden shortness of the hybrid peas he called a *recessive* character.

When Mendel's work was rediscovered, biologists began to extend the new science of genetics. They found, for instance, that the human eye obeys the Mendelian rule. Brown is dominant over blue, so that two blue-eyed parents cannot (with rare exceptions) beget a brown-eyed child. But two brown-eyed parents, each carrying a recessive gene capable of producing blue eyes, can engender blue-eyed children. Not all characters act this way. In some flowers, for instance, a cross between a red and a white variety gives an intermediate pink shade.

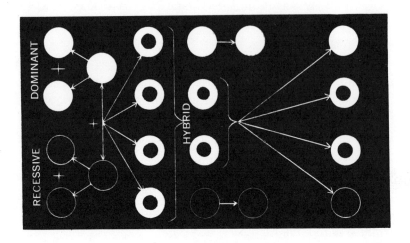

Diagram showing the results of matings between organisms carrying a recessive gene, between organisms carrying a dominant gene, and between organisms of the two different kinds. The white circles with smaller black circles inside them represent offspring of mixed type, in which the recessive character exists in hidden form and can be passed on.

Biologists also learned that hereditary characters sometimes underwent sudden changes called *mutations*. These mutations brought new characters into the hereditary makeup of the species and so gave evolution something to work on.

They learned that all the more complicated many-celled living things are made up of cells of two kinds: body cells, and sex cells or *gametes*. To start a body growing, two gametes, one male and one female, unite to form a single cell, called a *zygote*. This process is called fertilization or conception. The zygote then divides, grows, and divides again, until a complete working body has been formed. When this body becomes mature it, in turn, produces gametes. (There are many variations and exceptions among primitive plants and animals—the dandelion, for instance—but the system just described holds good for most of the plants and animals that we know.)

Every cell in the bodies of the higher plants and animals is made of two parts. The outer part is called the *cytoplasm*. Most of the master plan or directions for running the cell are in a small central part called the *nucleus*. Here are microscopic threadlike particles called *chromosomes*. When a cell is about to divide, the chromosomes do a kind of dance. Each splits lengthwise into two complete new chromosomes. One chromosome of each of these pairs moves toward one end of the cell while the other moves away from it. Thus when the cell divides, each daughter cell has a complete set of chromosomes. The chromosomes in a body cell come in pairs, each pair differing from every other. Human beings have twenty-three pairs (forty-six altogether) in each of their body cells. On the other hand, the tiny vinegar fly *Drosophila*, which swarms around decaying fruit, has four pairs (eight altogether).

When an organism reproduces sexually, one of the cells in its sexual organs divides and re-divides. The second time it divides, however, the chromosomes fail to duplicate themselves, so that the resulting cell has only half the usual zygote number: twenty-three in man and four in the vinegar fly. When conception takes place, the chromosomes of the two gametes are added together in the zygote, once more completing the double set—forty-six in man and eight in the vinegar fly.

A young American biologist, William S. Sutton (1876–1916), in 1902 realized that the Mendelian units of heredity were carried by the chromosomes. However, the major work on chromosomes was done by Thomas Hunt Morgan (1866–1945), a Kentuckian from a horse-breeding family, who became a professor at Columbia University in 1904.

Morgan's experimental animal was the vinegar fly *Drosoph-*

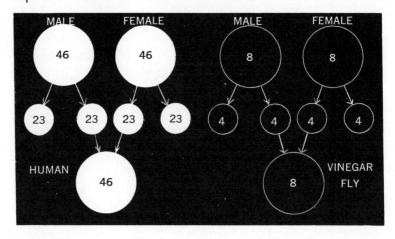

Diagram showing how, in sexual reproduction, a sex cell divides without duplication of chromosomes, producing daughter cells with half the normal number of chromosomes, and how two such cells unite at conception to form a cell with the full number.

ila. It makes a fine animal for the purpose, because it is easy and cheap to raise in large numbers and because it goes through its whole life cycle from egg to egg-laying adult in a mere ten days, compared to twenty-odd years for a man. Morgan and his assistants raised millions of these flies in jars and fed them on the yeast that grows on bits of banana and on cardboard soaked in syrup. They kept elaborate pedigrees of the flies by means of labels and card files.

Morgan was looking for mutations. After months of work, he found one: a male fly with white eyes instead of red. The white-eyed fly, mated to a normal female red-eyed fly, produced 1,237 offspring. When these were inbred, they brought forth red-eyed and white-eyed flies in the Mendelian ratio. As time passed, Morgan found more mutations: flies with eyes of various colors, or no eyes at all; flies with deformed wings or none; giant flies, dwarf flies, and so on.

Morgan, a slight man with a dark pointed beard and a suavely courteous manner, found that hereditary traits are carried by particles called *genes*. Each chromosome is a long string of genes, arranged somewhat like beads on a thread. A human zygote contains, some think, about 40,000 genes; others guess the number as high as a million. Each gene is a complicated molecule, which controls the development of one or more organs in the body of an animal or a plant. Morgan and his assistants also worked out, by a painstaking statistical method, the places where many genes are located along the chromosome strings.

In 1928, Morgan moved his researches to California Institute of Technology. He received the Nobel Prize in 1933. Although he retired in 1941, he kept on working almost to the day of his death.

Morgan's former assistant Hermann J. Muller also made important discoveries about mutations in the genes. In 1927, he found that exposing *Drosophila* flies to X rays increased their mutation rate 150 times. The next year, he learned that sudden changes of temperature also increased this mutation rate, although this is not necessarily true of larger organisms like man. At the same time, L. J. Stadler showed that X rays likewise produced mutations in plants. Others discovered that certain chemicals, such as the nitrogen mustards and formaldehyde, also raise the mutations rate.

And so, at last, one of the main questions about evolution was answered. How do variations in organisms get started? Organisms vary when penetrating radiations, temperature changes, certain chemicals, or other influences interfere with the workings of the delicate chromosome mechanism in their sex cells. The changes brought about by these influences are passed on to the next generation, unless they are so harmful that the creatures die before they grow old enough to reproduce. The final question was this: how are these changes passed along to the next generation?

The discoveries of Morgan, Muller, and their colleagues, during the last quarter-century, have increased man's knowledge almost as much as the earlier discoveries of Darwin and Mendel. Scientists have closed in upon the very nature of life itself. The largest share of this research on "the genetic code" has been done in the United States, although valuable contributions have also been made in Great Britain, Germany, and France.

It has taken very careful detective work to discover what genes and chromosomes are made of. During the nineteenth century, it became evident that living matter was mainly made up of substances of three kinds: carbohydrates, lipids, and proteins. Then around 1870, a young German chemist, Friedrich Miescher (1844–95), isolated a substance from the nuclei of cells that was neither carbohydrate, lipid, nor protein. It came to be known as *nucleic acid,* although like almost all organic acids it was, chemically speaking, an extremely weak acid.

Only a few chemists studied nucleic acid over the next three-quarters of a century. They did learn, however, that each molecule of nucleic acid is made up of a string of smaller particles, which they called *nucleotides.* Then, after the Second World War, a great deal of research was done on genes. Scientists learned that a gene is made of nucleic acid, and that the nucleotides in a gene are joined together in a long chain. They also learned that there are two types of nucleic acid. Because their chemical names are very long, they are usually called RNA (ribonucleic acid) and DNA (deoxyribonucleic acid) for short.

In 1953, two scientists at Cambridge University—the Briton Francis H. C. Crick and the American John D. Watson—discovered the structure of nucleic acids by shooting X rays through them and recording the divergence of these rays on a photographic plate. They inferred that every molecule of nucleic acid is built up into something like a ladder twisted into a corkscrew shape. This twisted ladder is a gene, which is DNA with its nucleotides arranged in a certain order.

It takes thousands of these ladderlike genes to make up one

chromosome. It is not yet known just how the genes are arranged in a chromosome; but this, too, may soon be learned.

The process of reproduction within a cell is quite complicated. A DNA molecule in the nucleus consists of four kinds of nucleotides, arranged just so. This DNA molecule manufactures a molecule of RNA, which is also made up of four kinds of nucleotides in a certain order. (Three of these are the same as in the DNA molecule; the fourth is different.) Each nucleotide of the DNA molecule is always paired with a nucleotide of one other kind in the RNA molecule, so the arrangement of nucleotides in the DNA molecule determines that in the RNA molecule.

Then the RNA molecule leaves the nucleus and moves into the cytoplasm, the outer part of the cell. Here it settles down to the manufacture of protein molecules. Protein molecules are made up of strings of sub-molecules of organic acids, called amino acids. There are twenty-two kinds of amino acids, combined in various ways to make up an enormous number of different proteins, which in turn make up a large part of our living substances.

The "code" is an arrangement whereby each set of three of the RNA molecule's nucleotides corresponds to one and only one kind of amino acid. A molecule of a particular kind of amino acid becomes fixed to the first three nucleotides of the RNA molecule; a molecule of another kind of amino acid to the next three nucleotides; and so on down the line until a complete protein molecule is formed. Other chemicals move the amino acids into positions in the chain and couple them together. When all is complete, the protein molecule breaks loose from the RNA molecule and goes about its business within the cell and along the blood stream.

The probable cause of most mutations is the loss of a nucleotide from a gene or an RNA molecule, or the addition of a nucleotide, or the substitution of the wrong nucleotide for the right one. Since the nucleotides in the RNA molecule work in groups of three, the loss or addition of one makes nonsense of the original DNA molecule's message from that point on. It is as if you had to write a sentence of three-letter words, like this:

THE BIG FAT MAN WAS ALL WET

If, however, you forgot one letter but continued to divide the remaining letters into groups of three, you would have something like:

THE IGF ATM ANW ASA LLW ET

You can see that the resulting sentence makes no sense at all.

Now, if the altered genetic message causes the plant or animal to be healthier, stronger, or better suited to the country it lives in, then the mutation will be passed on to its offspring and will spread through the species. But if, as is far more often the case, the mutation is harmful, then the organism will tend to die earlier than its forebears and so will leave fewer descendants or none at all. Hence, this mutation will disappear from the species. So now we have the answer Darwin was seeking when he wondered just how several different species could arise from one common ancestor over the centuries.

The biochemical discoveries of our times follow swiftly on each other's heels. Since the Second World War, discoveries in the field of genetics, plus improvements in the electron microscope, have settled the nature of viruses, those genelike organisms on the boundary between living and nonliving things. The chemical makeup of some of the larger and more complex proteins has also been solved. Someday scientists may even produce living cells from their chemical components; then we may know exactly how life might have originated on our earth many billions of years ago.

Although nowadays we hear more about space ships and nuclear power, current advances in the biological sciences may in time have even greater effects upon our lives. Such knowledge may lengthen human life to several times its present span, control genetic defects or even eliminate them, and possibly heighten the mental and physical powers of human beings.

XII · THE MOST MARVELOUS MACHINE

From the time that the first ape man had wit enough to grasp an oval stone and use its sharper end as a knife, man has been interested in the processes of birth and the causes of death, in curing his bodily ills, and in revealing the inner workings of his mind. The bodies of mummies prove that major surgical operations were performed in ancient Egypt more that 4,000 years ago; and written accounts of the treatments used by Greek doctors in their rest houses show man's concern for his health, centuries before the Christian Era. We also have accounts of astonishingly accurate diagnoses of diseases made by famous Muslim physicians who practiced in the Near East during the Dark Ages in Europe.

Nevertheless, as medieval Europe transformed itself into the alert, commerce-minded, city-studded Renaissance world of the days of Columbus, no definite cures had yet been discovered for any disease. Throughout Europe, the practice of medicine was little better than the practice of magic; and the doctors in America, even more backward than those in the lands from which they came, knew even less than their European colleagues. During the Revolutionary War, nine times as many American soldiers died from disease as from British bullets and bayonets.

There were several reasons for this dismal state of affairs.

For one thing, no one understood the role of germs in disease and the urgent need for medical cleanliness or antisepsis. For another, many instruments in common use today had yet to be invented. There existed no stethoscope for listening to the heart, no thermometer for checking a patient's fever, no hypodermic needles for injecting medicines into a patient's arm. In fact, there were few medicines to give in any way.

Although doctors had considerable knowledge of human anatomy and were able to make quite accurate diagnoses, their ideas of proper treatment were primitive. Time-honored but mistaken practices were handed down through generations, such as "cupping" or "leeching," common even in George Washington's time. Instead of giving weak patients transfusions of blood, as is done today, physicians drained their blood from them, thereby further reducing their chances of survival.

Furthermore, few men with any medical experience at all were to be found outside the cities, which huddled along the eastern seaboard. The farm folk, who lived in scattered communities along winding muddy roads, had to rely on the neighborly help of local women. The pioneer families beyond the Alleghenies had more to fear than Indians and loneliness; they had no one at all to help them when they lay injured or ill.

In those days, the general public was ignorant and superstitious. They could not distinguish between a quack who sold them "elixirs of life" said to cure all ills, or charms to ward off all diseases, and a legitimate physician who, it must be admitted, could seldom do more than reassure the patient and hope that time would cure him. Moreover, so many people thought it sinful to disturb the dead that medical students had great difficulty obtaining bodies for dissection. Yet, unless a doctor has studied the actual appearance and location of all the organs of the body, he cannot perform a successful operation on a living person. For that matter, not much successful surgery could be performed before the discovery of anesthetics and antiseptics.

Finally, the human body is a marvelous but very complicated machine—vastly more complicated than a diesel engine or even a computer. Since the body has considerable powers of curing itself, it is hard for a doctor always to tell whether a medicine is effective or whether the person is on the mend in any case. For all these reasons, medicine long lagged behind the other sciences.

Around the middle of the nineteenth century, a revolution in medicine was set in motion by Drs. Oliver Wendell Holmes (1809–94) in the United States and Ignaz P. Semmelweis (1818–65) in Austria, who demanded that physicians clean their hands and instruments much more thoroughly than had been the custom, in order not to carry infections from one patient to another. Incredible as it may seem to us, their colleagues at first thought them mad.

In the 1860s and 70s, the French chemist Louis Pasteur (1822–95) and the German physician Robert Koch (1843–1910) proved that many diseases were caused by bacteria or germs. Shortly afterward, Sir Joseph Lister (1827–1912) brought into regular use in England the practice of antisepsis —scrupulous medical cleanliness and the use of germ-killing liquids in surgical operations.

In addition to proving the germ theory of disease, Pasteur founded the science of immunology. One day in 1879, he came upon a pot of old broth made of chicken gristle in which he had been growing chicken-cholera germs a few weeks before. He studied this broth and injected some of it into his laboratory chickens. He found that the solution would no longer give the chickens the disease of cholera. In fact, it had the opposite effect: it made them immune to further attacks of cholera. He had unknowingly made a vaccine.

Pasteur put his new-found knowledge to good use when he discovered how to create a vaccine for rabies. Rabies is an agonizing disease of the nervous system, which was always fatal to human beings bitten by a rabid animal. After six years of work on a virus too small to be seen in any microscope of the time, Pasteur learned how to locate the virus, how to keep it alive in the brains of rabbits, and how to transplant it from one rabbit's brain to another until it lost its deadly qualities without losing its power to protect a human being inoculated with it.

Other important things were happening in nineteenth-century Europe. Several scientists discovered that the body is made up of millions of coöperating cells. In the 1890s, Wilhelm K. Roentgen invented the X ray and made it possible for the first time to peer into a human body without cutting it open.

Although American medicine slumbered fitfully through the early years of the medical revolution, a few doctors made significant contributions to the growing mass of medical knowledge. In 1822, William Beaumont (1785–1853), a U. S. Army surgeon stationed in the Great Lakes region, tended a young French Canadian named Alexis St. Martin (1801–81), whose stomach had been blown open by an accidental gun shot. The wound healed so as to leave a hole in the skin of St. Martin's belly and another hole in the stomach itself, with flaps of muscular tissue keeping the holes partially closed.

Beaumont persuaded St. Martin to let himself be used as a human laboratory. For several years, the surgeon kept the unfortunate St. Martin as a hired man. He regularly peered into the young man's stomach, pushed bits of food tied to strings through the holes, and later pulled them out again to see how far they had been digested.

Beaumont's reports made medical history; but he and St. Martin came to hate each other. Beaumont was an arrogant, domineering man who bullied the illiterate backwoodsman until the poor fellow took to drink. Tired of being roared at, St. Martin ran away; was lured back by offers of higher pay; then ran away again, this time for good.

However, the outstanding American medical achievement of

the nineteenth century was the discovery of anesthesia in the 1840s by Long and Morton. William Thomas Green Morton (1819–68) was a dentist in Boston who had invented an improved dental plate. But, before he could install this plate, Morton had to remove all of the patient's remaining teeth. To make the operation painless, he tried several anesthetics and found that ether worked best. Although Dr. Crawford W. Long (1815–78) of Georgia had already used ether in a minor operation, he had never attempted to explain his discovery to other doctors.

Morton, on the other hand, demonstrated his method of painless operations by anesthetizing a patient for the surgeon Dr. John C. Warren (1778–1856). After the astonished Dr. Warren had successfully removed a tumor from the face of his unconscious patient, he turned to the assembled physicians and said: "Gentlemen, this is no humbug." [1]

Morton next obtained a patent on the use of ether in operations, for which modern physicians sometimes condemn him as unethical. It must be remembered that Morton was a dentist, not a physician; and no dentist of his time would have seen anything wrong with this procedure. However, Morton found it impossible to enforce his monopoly on the use of ether. He had no way of knowing just when and how often some other physician pressed a spongeful of ether to his patients' noses.

Since he found his patent unenforceable, Morton spent years trying to make Congress award him a cash grant for his services to humanity. This plan was thwarted by several rivals, each of whom claimed to be the true discoverer of anesthesia. The most persistent of these rivals was Charles Thomas Jackson (1805–80), a geologist from whom Morton had sought advice in the early stages of his discovery. Jackson cruelly persecuted Morton, who spent the rest of his life in and out of court fighting Jackson's claims and campaigning for the fortune that he felt the world owed him.

As a final blow, in 1862, the U. S. Supreme Court decided

that Morton's patent was invalid (not legally sound). The Court held that the patent claimed a monopoly on a law of nature, whereas American law allows patents only on new and useful processes, substances, machines, and manufactured articles.

Morton served as a volunteer anesthetist during the Civil War and then, poor and worn out, retired to a farm. He died of apoplexy brought on by reading an article supporting the claims of his hated foe Jackson. But Jackson's victory did him no good; he went violently insane and spent the last seven years of his life in an asylum.

Although Morton's anesthesia stands with Lister's antisepsis and Pasteur's germ theory of disease as one of the three outstanding advances of nineteenth-century medicine, toward the end of the century the medical schools of Europe were still far ahead of ours. Young doctors tried, if possible, to study abroad, in order to see the new techniques in use and to meet the world's leading medical authorities.

These new discoveries and techniques were finally brought back to the United States by several of these traveling students. One of them, William Henry Welch (1850–1934), toured the laboratories of Europe in order to prepare himself for the professorship in pathology at Johns Hopkins University in Baltimore. Here he held sway over several generations of medical students—a huge, bald, jowly, untidy man with a white mustache and goatee, who encouraged young doctors to do research in medicine and who eventually became the subject of many a legend.

Slowly America caught up with the best brains of Europe. Some medical men began to spend their lives on research, learning how the body works and how to make it function better. Such men are called physiologists; their science, physiology. Medicine is the art of applying these findings to individual patients; and the doctors who so apply them are physicians. At the turn of the century, physicians began to specialize in the various fields of medicine, because a man could no longer master all that was now known about the human body.

Private foundations, set up by men like Rockefeller and Carnegie, advanced large sums to the universities where much of the medical research was in progress. As drugs to fight different diseases were developed, and as the drug companies grew powerful and rich, they, too, began sponsoring research into the causes of disease and the development of better medicines. The U. S. Government became interested in promoting the health and psychological welfare of its armed forces and, more recently, of its general population as well, and so began to make grants to solve specific health problems.

For example, a team of American army doctors, headed by Walter Reed (1851–1902), found the cause of yellow fever, which was killing off American soldiers stationed in Cuba after the Spanish-American War. Proof that certain mosquitoes spread the disease was furnished by a soldier, Private Kissinger, and a civilian, John J. Moran. These men risked their lives when they volunteered to let themselves be bitten by the mosquitoes; they came down with yellow fever but fortunately recovered. Methods of mosquito control were soon developed and wiped out the plagues of yellow fever that, for more than a hundred and fifty years, had each summer terrorized the people of marshland cities like Philadelphia.

For many centuries, man had attributed plagues to the wrath of God or to the evil spells of witches. The physician to King Louis XIV of France smiled at the "absurd" idea of some of his seventeenth-century colleagues, who believed that several diseases were caused by "a numerous School of little nimble, brisk invisible living things, of a very prolific Nature, which when once admitted, increase, and multiply in Aboundance." [2] Yet the organisms that caused most diseases had been visible ever since the Dutchman Anton van Leeuwenhoek [3] (1632–1723) invented the microscope in the 1670s.

These "brisk invisible living things" were bacteria, which

proved to be more like plants than animals in their chemistry, which average 1/25,000 of an inch in length, and which are shaped like ovals, balls, rods, or corkscrews. Strangely enough, even after bacteria had been discovered and described by Leeuwenhoek, it took two centuries for science to establish the connection between these swarming organisms and the diseases they cause.

After Pasteur proved that bacteria can cause disease, researchers soon discovered that there are many kinds of disease-bearing bacteria, that some affect only people, that some affect only animals, that some affect only plants of various sorts, and that some live harmlessly in soil or water. They learned to grow bacteria in nourishing bouillon solutions, or on the surface of a jelly, and to make vaccines from them for the protection of plants and animals. Other men learned that, against invading bacteria, the body summons up an army of tiny leucocytes or white corpuscles, that swarm around the invaders and engulf them, then stand guard against a further onslaught of the offending bacteria. Therefore, if a few bacteria of less deadly strains are introduced into the blood stream, a person or an animal can marshal his forces against not only these attenuated or weakened strains but also against future attacks of more dangerous bacteria of the same kind.

However, for a long time, medical researchers were perplexed by a number of diseases, which acted like diseases caused by bacteria but for which no bacteria could be found. At the turn of the century, it was discovered that some invisible organism, so small that it could go right through a porcelain filter, could still cause disease. This minute creature— much smaller than a bacterium—was called a virus; and men wondered whether it was a living creature or a poisonous chemical. They also wondered if they would ever find a way to see it.

Wendell M. Stanley, a chemist at the Princeton, New Jersey, laboratories of the Rockefeller Institute, was searching for a virus that might be the cause of tobacco mosaic, a disease that spots the leaves of tobacco plants. During 1934–35, Stanley ground up infected plants, soaked them until they became a kind of soup, treated the soup with chemicals, and repeatedly filtered them. At last, he eliminated everything except water and the invisible viruses; then, by adding a chemical, he caused the virus to form needle-like crystals large enough to be seen in an ordinary microscope. When dissolved, the substance of the crystals proved as infectious as ever to tobacco plants. Thus, Stanley was the first man to see a group of viruses; and, for this feat, he received a Nobel Prize.

The invention of the electron microscope in the 1930s enabled research men to see the outline of a single virus. In such a microscope, electrons shot through a tube are stopped by even a tiny, transparent object, while the other electrons continue through the tube and spread out to fill in the background of an image on a screen. So, now men could see a virus in silhouette.

Then, in the 1940s, Robert C. Williams at the University of Michigan learned how to plate, with a thin film of metal, objects as small as viruses, so that they could be seen in electron-microscope photographs. At last men could see viruses and study them! Soon they discovered that viruses are particles that act in some ways like chemical molecules and in other ways like living things. In short, they are a link between the two.

Since that time, more than 150 different kinds of viruses that attack man and many that attack plants and animals have been isolated. In 1931, Ernest Goodpasture and his associates, C. Eugene Woodruff and his wife, Alice Woodruff, worked out an inexpensive method of cultivating viruses in hens' eggs so that they could be used for immunizing living things against them.

Other experimenters discovered that the presence of hostile viruses in a body stimulates certain glands and tissues to secrete chemicals that combine with the viruses and render them harmless. These chemicals are called *antibodies;* and each different virus must be neutralized by a different antibody. While some antibodies disappear after they are no longer needed, others remain in the blood stream for years, ready to combine with any new invasion of viruses of the same type. This is the principle underlying inoculation against virus diseases.

The most publicized virus has been that which causes poliomyelitis or infantile paralysis, a disease which had become more prevalent in the twentieth century. Strangely enough, increased sanitation brought about the increase! In unsanitary countries, nearly everybody was exposed to the disease while still an infant, equipped with natural antibodies that rendered the virus harmless. Under conditions of modern sanitation, few infants are exposed to polio; thus, when it attacks them as older children or young adults, they have no immunity to it.

In 1938, President Franklin D. Roosevelt, himself a victim of poliomyelitis, launched the National Foundation for Infantile Paralysis and interested the public in supporting it with gifts to the March of Dimes. Efforts to make a polio vaccine were unsuccessful for fifteen years. At last, in 1954, Jonas E. Salk, a quiet young virologist working at a hospital in Pittsburgh with Foundation money, made a vaccine from dead viruses. An overhasty, nation-wide campaign to vaccinate all children and many adults with this vaccine (without allowing time for manufacturing methods to be perfected) resulted in a couple of hundred man-induced cases of polio; but the following year saw an enormous decline in the incidence of this disease.

In the meantime, a colleague of Dr. Salk, Albert Sabin, was busy developing a vaccine made from live polio viruses that had been attenuated, or weakened with age. Although medical men still disagree as to whether live or killed viruses are better or safer, the control of polio is now so complete that, with proper precautions, no child in America need fear the crippling effects of this disease.

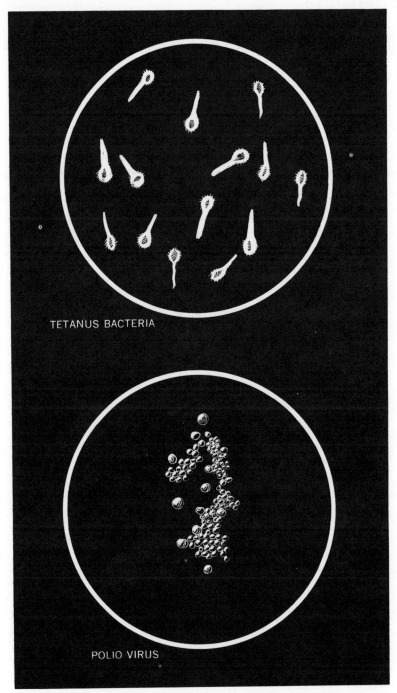

TETANUS BACTERIA

POLIO VIRUS

MICROSCOPIC ORGANISMS THAT CAUSE DISEASES

The present century has seen the conquest of many virus-borne diseases besides rabies, yellow fever, and infantile paralysis. Virus pneumonia, influenza, measles, mumps, hepatitis, and the common cold have all yielded to some degree to injections designed to ban or to reduce the severity of these diseases.

The study of the human body includes much more than the size, shape, and workings of the various organs, and the behavior of the germs and other organisms that invade the body from the outside. It includes a knowledge of the chemical compounds of which organs and organisms are made, of the chemicals they secrete, and of the effect of still other chemicals introduced into the body as food, drugs, and poisons. This study forms the science of biochemistry, the largest, most complicated, fastest-growing branch of chemistry of the mid-twentieth century.

A study of the ductless glands and of the hormones or "chemical messengers" they secrete began about half a century ago. Hormones are necessary for normal development, for metabolism, and for reproduction, even for the maintenance of life itself. Minute amounts of them affect growth, stimulate the nervous system, coördinate digestive activities, and interact to maintain all the bodily functions.

If one ductless gland fails to produce the correct amount of one hormone, the whole system is upset. For example, if the pancreas does not produce enough insulin in the body, a disorder called diabetes results. Before 1921, diabetes always proved fatal. In that year, a group of physicians, including Sir Frederick Grant Banting (1891–1941), the Scottish physiologist; John J. R. Macleod (1876–1935), who long taught at Western Reserve University; Charles H. Best, of the University of Toronto; and James B. Collip, a Canadian, discovered a way to make insulin that could be used to offset diabetes. Now, persons suffering from this degenerative disorder—it is not an infectious disease—can expect to live about as long as anyone else.

Another outstanding achievement of this century was the discovery of the role played by other biochemicals called vitamins in the proper nutrition of humans and other animals. The name "vitamine" was coined in 1912 by a Polish chemist, Casimir Funk; but much of the work on vitamins has been done in the United States.

Deficiency diseases were known long before their causes and cures. Sailors, who were forced to spend long months at sea and to eat salted meats without any fresh vegetables, learned that the often fatal disease of scurvy could be prevented by eating limes regularly. They did not know that limes (like oranges) were a concentrated source of vitamin C; but they did know that limes could be kept on board for several months.

Similarly, although no one knew that vitamins A and B were to be found in cod-liver oil, careful parents for several generations gave this evil-smelling substance to young children during the sunless winter months because it kept them rosy and well. And, although no one knew until the 1920s that liver was rich in vitamin B_1, doctors urged their anemic patients to eat liver regularly to give them energy.

Today, no one need suffer from vitamin deficiency. Good eating habits can be formed by everyone; and for those with serious deficiencies, synthetic vitamins have become available in capsule form. Doctors still do not know all that is to be known about the effect of one vitamin upon another or how to determine precisely whether a patient is getting the correct optimum amount of these minute substances in his daily diet. Complete understanding of the role of vitamins will undoubtedly be worked out in time.

Another group of biochemicals are the antibiotics, substances that kill bacteria without destroying the normal cells of the body. Most of the earlier-known germ-killers destroyed bacteria effectively but damaged human tissue as well.

The first antibiotic ever discovered was penicillin, made by a common mold, which Alexander Fleming (1881–1955), a small, silent Scotsman, found by accident in 1928. At the University of London, somebody had forgotten to close a laboratory window, and the wind had blown mold spores into the room. They settled on some flat glass dishes containing agar, a jelly made from seaweed, in which Fleming was raising a crop of experimental bacteria. The spores promptly grew into mold plants and killed the surrounding germs.

The minute amount of the germ-killing substance given out by the mold was much too rare in those days for general medical use. Two Britons, Howard W. Florey and Ernest B. Chain, began investigating ways to obtain penicillin in larger quantities. During the Second World War, when huge quantities of the drug were needed, the United States became interested in their researches and invited them to continue their efforts at the Department of Agriculture laboratory at Peoria, Illinois. Florey took charge of the laboratory and, despite great difficulties, managed to mass-produce penicillin in 1943.

Other antibiotics were being studied at the time that penicillin was found. German medical researchers discovered the sulfonamids, which became popular until doctors learned that they must be used with care to avoid harming the patient. Later, the Russian-born Selman A. Waksman, working at Rutgers University in New Jersey, discovered streptomycin. This drug proved to be the first of another family of antibiotics made by microscopic organisms that live in the soil.

As a result of the discovery of these and numerous other miracle-working drugs and the increasing skill of doctors in prescribing treatment with them, the death rate over much of the earth has been lowered to an extent that would have seemed fantastic in George Washington's time. Nowadays, in the more advanced countries, nearly everybody has a good chance of living to old age; whereas formerly, very few people succeeded in doing so.

The medical revolution, however, has brought grave new problems with it. In many lands, modern medicine has enabled people to increase so fast that the population doubles every twenty-five or thirty years. Eventually, such countries are certain to run out of space in which to grow food; in fact, some of them already have done so. Then, unless the growth of population is halted in some other way, Malthus's grim prediction of the limitation of numbers by starvation is bound to come true.

Another problem, which may prove as important in the long run as the danger of mass starvation, is that of the growing number of hereditary defects in the population of the earth. Modern medicine enables millions of people with inherited defects of body or mind to live normal life spans and to pass their imperfections on to their children. Under primitive conditions of health and sanitation, people born with severe mental or physical defects usually died young and never became parents. Because most mutations are harmful, the number of people bearing these defects is likely to increase until, thousands of years hence, despite the wonders of medicine, the human species will have a hard time surviving at all.

From earliest times, men have been interested in the human mind, particularly in those minds that seemed to be disordered. In medieval times and for centuries thereafter, it was customary to mistreat the mentally ill in order to drive out the devils in control of them. Even in England, in the seventeenth and eighteenth centuries, these unfortunate people were kept in dark cellars, sometimes chained to the wall, and treated as if they were criminals of the worst sort.

As medical knowledge grew during the nineteenth century, doctors began to realize that the mind is intimately connected with the body and that ways ought to be devised to study it. The study of the mind is called psychology. The branch of psychology that deals with the treatment of sick or deranged minds is psychiatry. Studies were made by European scientists into the main causes of mental illness; and patients were given rest cures and more kindly treatment. Nevertheless, not a great deal could be done until more was learned about the functioning of the brain and the nervous system and the causes of the various mental abnormalities.

Toward the end of the nineteenth century, the leader of American psychology was the slight, bearded, blue-eyed William James (1842–1910). Brother of Henry James the novelist, William James was a man of lively, generous, impulsive, and altogether charming personality. After studying at Harvard and in Germany, James suffered a five-year nervous breakdown during which he could only sit and brood. Then, recovering, he became a professor at Harvard and wrote a great textbook on psychology, which long remained the standard work in its field.

In the 1870s, James set up the first American laboratory of experimental psychology. For years, he labored in two little rooms in the Scientific School building at Harvard, until the rooms became jammed with apparatus. James was not very good at experimental work because it tired him out to concentrate on one thing for very long. When his successor, the German psychologist Hugo Münsterberg (1863–1916) arrived, James gladly turned the laboratory over to him.

James was a man of many interests. He studied philosophy and religion from a scientific point of view. He investigated strange and doubtful phenomena like the claims of Spiritualist mediums that they could speak with the spirits of the dead. He was a great personality rather than a deep thinker. Still, his influence was strong; some of the policies of President Franklin D. Roosevelt were based on James's teachings, with their accent on the practical result of one's actions rather than on their abstract rightness or wrongness.

In James's time, a revolution in psychology was beginning in Europe under the leadership of the Austrian psychiatrist Sigmund Freud (1856–1939). Freud taught that the mind is like an iceberg, seven-eighths of which is out of sight. The part of which we are aware is called the conscious mind; the rest is the unconscious or subconscious. People's acts are, to a large extent, ruled by the subconscious mind, which in turn is influenced by the experiences of early childhood and the habits formed then.

Freud believed that the working of the subconscious mind could sometimes be uncovered by a study of a person's dreams. He thought that some mental disturbances could be cleared up by bringing subconscious conflicts into the patient's conscious mind and making him aware of what was bothering him. This technique is called psychoanalysis. Because of these and other interesting theories, Freud gathered a group of disciples in Vienna. But, when some of his followers developed different theories of their own, he quarreled with them. His early pupil Carl G. Jung (1875–1961) developed the idea of introverted and extroverted personalities; while Alfred Adler (1870–1937), another pupil, stated that a sense of inferiority is one of the strongest motivating forces behind human personalities.

In 1909, Clark University in Massachusetts held a psychological conference, attended by many of the outstanding psychological minds of the age. Freud, a small man with a neat white beard—dry, tart, and coolly impersonal—arrived to lecture. During a recess, Freud and James strolled out to talk. Unfortunately, no cosmic thoughts were exchanged; for James became suddenly ill, and had to gulp medicine and wait for the attack to pass.

Freud went back to Vienna, grumbling sourly about American food. Although Freud always disliked the United States, Americans took up Freudian psychology with enthusiasm. In the 1920s and 30s, hot disputes over his teachings raged among the various schools of psychologists and psychiatrists. At length, doctrines that seemed to square with the facts were accepted, while those that did not were quietly dropped.

Interest was not confined to disordered minds in the early years of this century. In order to understand normal human brains and personalities, tests had to be devised and given to large numbers of apparently normal people. The first intelligence test was prepared in 1905 by the French psychologist Alfred Binet (1857–1911), who used it to investigate scholastically retarded school children. This test was given orally and so could measure relatively few children. Therefore, in 1916, the American psychologist Lewis Madison Terman and his associates at Stanford University revised the Binet test so that older children could give their answers in writing. The most notable innovation of Terman's revision was the introduction of the concept of *intelligence quotient* or IQ, which tells by a simple number whether a child's mental age exceeds or falls short of the average for children of his chronological age. An IQ of 100 indicates normal intelligence; of 125 or above indicates a mind capable of profiting from a college education; of 75 or less indicates mental deficiency.

A later revision of the Stanford-Binet test is the Terman-Merrill Scale, which was devised in 1937 and which is today given to many American school children. In recent years, other tests have been developed to test for scholastic aptitude, for personality, and for specific abilities required for certain jobs. A modern young person can find out from school advisers and testing bureaus how well he measures up to the norms and in which lines of work he is likely to succeed. Everyone should know as much as possible about his own mind as well as about his body, so that he can plan a way of life that will prove satisfying to him.

Other twentieth-century psychologists studied how habits are formed and how personalities are built. The Russian psychologist Ivan Petrovitch Pavlov (1849–1936), experimenting with dogs, found out that if some sight or sound or thought repeatedly leads to a certain action, a dog or a person will develop a "conditioned reflex" or a habit. Likewise, the reflex can be de-conditioned, or the habit broken, if, for a number of times, the sight or sound or thought no longer leads to the same action. For example, if a child learns that by crying he can get his mother to give him candy, he will cry whenever he is denied. However, if his mother finally decides to break him of this habit and refuses candy whenever he cries for it, in time he will learn to substitute for crying some other action, such as asking politely or earning the candy by doing what he is told.

American psychologists long argued whether a personality was the result of the individual's heredity (the genes he inherited from his parents) or of his environment (the surroundings and education he had as a child). In the 1920s and 30s, many taught that environment must be practically the only important influence on personality development; for they thought it would be unfair or undemocratic for one person to be born inferior to another.

However, with advances in the science of genetics (the study of the role of genes in passing parents' attributes on to their children), it became plain that most of an individual's characteristics were the result of *both* heredity and environment. Although such things as the color of a person's eyes were entirely governed by heredity, and his language entirely by environment, most of his qualities were a result of the two forces acting together. Heredity started the individual in a certain direction and set limits to his development; the kind of home and schooling he had modified him in one direction or another within those limits.

Several studies of identical twins brought up in two different environments have been made, among them the study made by H. H. Newman, F. N. Freeman, and K. J. Holzinger of the University of Chicago. These workers followed the lives of a number of twins who had been separated by the death of their parents and adopted into homes of quite different sorts. In the 1930s, these psychologists reported that although these identical twins developed manners, customs, and points of view current in their separate environments, their physical appearance and their mental powers remained much alike and thus must have been determined by heredity. Similar studies during the last thirty years indicate that, of the two forces—heredity and environment—heredity in most respects has the stronger influence in making us what we are. The results of such studies as these show that it is of the utmost importance to provide a child with a good environment, so that he can develop his entire hereditary potential.

Since the 1930s, a great deal has been learned about sick minds as well as about normal growth and development. People with psychological problems or serious mental illness can find sound treatment in clinics or in the offices of private psychiatrists. A new trend in the treatment of mental illness is pharmacotherapy, the treatment of mental disorders with drugs that stimulate persons suffering from severe depressions and quiet those in states of agitation and excitement. Although these drugs are still in the experimental stage, the joining of psychology with biochemistry may soon restore to health many people who are not responding to purely psychological treatments for mental disorders.

In the next century, new medicines and increased knowledge of the human mind may be combined to eliminate much human suffering and to free from mental hospitals many people who are presently considered beyond hope. More important still, many of today's children may grow up free from the illnesses and fears that limited full human development in the centuries before men knew much about the sciences of man.

XIII · THE SCIENCES OF MAN

Our earliest records show that man has always been interested in the world he lived in. He has tried to solve its riddles and to convert its forces and treasures to his use. He has also given considerable thought to himself and to the relationships among himself, his family, and his neighbors. However, until man had the ships and planes to travel to far places in order to study people in cultures very different from his own, and until he found out how to unearth the relics of great civilizations that flourished in centuries gone by, man was not able to view himself objectively nor to make valid comparisons between his culture and the rest. Only in the past hundred years or so has science been able to turn the spotlight of investigation on man himself.

The study of man has many aspects. We can view him as an individual and investigate the workings of his mind (psychology), the structure of his body (physiology), and the causes and cures of his illnesses (pathology). These sciences, which have made enormous strides in the past century, were discussed in the previous chapter.

We can also study man as part of a group. We can inquire into the behavior of the entire human species as compared to that of the other higher mammals; or we can study the actions of men as members of such communities as families, tribes, nations, and races. We can compare the behavior of modern men who live in cities with that of men in ancient Athens or Rome.

Three sciences deal with the study of man as part of a group. The first is anthropology, which concerns itself with man as the highest form of life found on this planet. *Physical anthropology* considers the physique of living men of various races and types. It studies skulls and other bones of former races of men to see how men have evolved and to predict what the man of the future will be like. *Social anthropology* investigates the behavior of men as members of the groups they live in.

Closely related to anthropology is archaeology, the study of the material remains of men who lived in former times. These remains include not only the bones of men, but also their tools, weapons, houses, jewelry, religious objects, and systems of transportation. With equal care, archaeologists uncover the flint axes of a cave man, the sunken ship of a Phoenician trader, and the tomb of an ancient Chinese emperor. By means of these archaeological finds, scientists try to fill in the yawning gaps in the written history of ancient, civilized peoples. They also strive to sketch an outline of the history of the more primitive peoples who, not knowing how to write, have left no written records at all.

The third of these sister sciences is *sociology,* the science of societies—a kind of natural history of the groups into which human beings organize themselves and of the way individuals react to life within this group. There is some overlap between sociology and social anthropology. Today, social anthropologists concern themselves mainly with the doings of primitive men living in scattered tribes, whereas the sociologists study the activities of civilized men living in nations of advanced culture.

The roots of the modern science of anthropology lie in the tales of ancient and medieval travelers about the peoples whom they encounter. Valuable as these narratives are, they leave much to be desired; for all men tend to look upon their own group, or tribe, or nation as the best people in the world, and their own manners and customs as the only right and decent ones. Among many primitive tribes, the people's name for themselves means "real human beings." Foreigners are not quite human and hence are often ill-treated.

Therefore, when a medieval European wrote about the strange people he met on his travels, he scorned as "beastly savages" those whose ways were very different from his own. Anthropology could not become scientific until men learned to look at people of other cultures without passing judgment upon them and without assuming that their own beliefs and customs were necessarily "right" and all others "wrong."

The science of anthropology got under way about a century ago. Physical anthropologists began the task—not yet completed—of classifying men into races according to their physical types. The first person to undertake this work was François Bernier, a seventeenth-century French physician and traveler. Bernier divided men into Europeans, Africans, and Asiatics. He considered the Lapps a distinct race and could not decide where to put the American Indians and the African Bushmen.

From Bernier's time to the present, many scientists have tried dividing men into races, the number of races ranging all the way from two to thirty-four. One tried dividing mankind on the basis of skin color: white and black. Another divided them according to the shape of their skulls: long-heads and broad-heads. Still others tried to classify them as straight-haired and woolly-haired. If one tries to classify people on the basis of one characteristic only, he finds that they will fall into quite a different arrangement when they are regrouped by some other characteristic. For example, if men are grouped by skin color alone, white men stand with yellow; if by skull form alone, white men stand partly with yellow men and partly with black.

Actually, men cannot be put into such neat pigeonholes as these classifications assume. The races of man shade gradually into one another without sharp boundaries, for the world is full of mixed and intermediate types.

Most modern anthropologists recognize three main races: the white or Caucasoid, the yellow or Mongoloid, and the black or Negroid. (The German anthropologist Johann F. Blumenbach [1752–1840] chose "Caucasian" as his name for the white race because he believed the people of the Caucasus Mountains to be the handsomest of all whites, and because he had a particularly fine skull from this region in his collection.) Each of these main races is made up of a mixture of subraces or types; thus the Caucasoid race includes the tall, long-headed, light-haired, blue-eyed Nordic type of northern Europe; the stocky, broad-headed Alpine type of central Europe; and the slight, dark, long-headed Mediterranean type from the region around the Mediterranean Sea. In addition, we find a few small groups like the Australian aborigines and the African Bushmen, which do not fit into any of the major groups and so are given the rank of separate races.

The latter part of the nineteenth century and the early part of the twentieth saw a widespread dispute over the question of which race was superior in intellect and character. Understandably, people who claimed superiority for a particular race or type themselves invariably belonged to that race or type; nobody has ever classed his own particular group as inferior. The loudest propagandists for such racial distinctions have been persons of northern European ancestry, who claimed the prize of perfection for the tall, blond, Nordic type of the Caucasoid race, sometimes miscalled the "Aryan race." Their arguments, however, were mere oratory and had no scientific basis.

Only a few American scientists, such as Henry Fairfield Osborn (1857–1935) the paleontologist, and William McDougall (1871–1938), the psychologist and sociologist, took the

Nordic-Aryan cult seriously; all the other major anthropologists considered it nonsense. At the same time, many people insisted, with equal fervor and just as little scientific knowledge, that all races had exactly the same mental equipment.

Nowadays, most anthropologists believe that the differences among races are, on the average, much less than the differences among the individuals of any one race. They also believe that there is no way at present to test people to determine whether one race is better—and if so, in what respects—than another. Unless all the children being tested grow up in the same culture, with equal opportunities, and speaking the same language, accurate tests to compare their inborn abilities cannot be designed. A fourteen-year-old boy in an Eskimo village would not know how to drive the family car, because there is no family car. Likewise, an ordinary American boy would not do very well on a test in which he had to kill a seal with an ivory harpoon on some Arctic ice floe.

Social anthropology, the study of the remaining primitive peoples, began in Europe in the nineteenth century with the work of men like Adolf Bastian (1826–1905) in Germany and Jacques Boucher de Perthes (1788–1868) in France. Bastian visited tribal societies all over the world, collected their tools and ornaments, and noted how they lived. Boucher de Perthes insisted that some curiously shaped pieces of flint, which had been found in Europe and which were called "thunder stones," were really the tools and weapons of primitive men. He showed a skeptical world that the ancestors of Europeans had once been as primitive as any modern savage.

In the United States, serious anthropological research began in the 1820s, when a young chemical engineer named Henry Rowe Schoolcraft (1793–1864) went on an Army expedition to the upper Mississippi. Schoolcraft started out to look for minerals but became interested in the Chippewa Indians of Minnesota. He married the granddaughter of a Chippewa chief and spent the rest of his life in that region, making his living as an Indian agent and politician. He spent his spare time gathering information about his wife's people and published his findings in several huge volumes. Longfellow's famous poem *Hiawatha* is based on the Chippewa myths collected by Schoolcraft.

The second American anthropologist was a lawyer turned painter. He was George Catlin (1796–1872), who set out from Pennsylvania in the 1830s to tour all the Indian tribes in order to paint them, and to gather and publish information about them because he thought that they were dying out and would soon be gone.

The Indians did not disappear, although their numbers dwindled throughout the century, mainly as a result of diseases caught from the white man. Nineteenth-century white Americans had little understanding of the Indians, whose cultures and languages were utterly different from their own. A few people thought of them as virtuous, noble red men. More, however, considered them dirty, thieving, treacherous heathens who did not deserve fair treatment and who ought to be wiped off the earth.

But the Indians were simply men and women with the usual human virtues and faults. Although they were often cheated, robbed, and massacred by the whites, the Indians acquired mighty champions among such American scientists as J. Wesley Powell, the geologist; O. C. Marsh, the paleontologist; and L. H. Morgan, the anthropologist. In the present century, they have increased in numbers and prosperity, although many of their old languages and customs have indeed fallen into disuse.

The outstanding American contribution to early anthropology was made by an upstate New York lawyer, financier, and politician named Lewis Henry Morgan (1818–81). As a youth, Morgan and some friends formed a club modeled on an Indian tribe. To learn how real Indians did things, they visited the nearby Iroquois reservation.

Morgan's interest in Indians became serious. He studied the Iroquois system of family relationships and discovered that similar systems prevailed among the Chippewas of Minnesota and also among the ancient Greeks and Romans. They divided themselves into family or kinship groups, which anthropologists call *clans*. Everybody in a clan is descended from one common ancestor. The clans have legal and political powers, and each one runs its own affairs as if it were a little tribe.

Morgan mistakenly concluded that this system applied to all primitive peoples. He worked out a theory of the development of human culture from "savagery" through "barbarism" to "civilization." He thought that the goal of all this striving, the supreme product of civilization, was a successful Christian American businessman like Lewis Henry Morgan. Even though later anthropologists found that human cultures do not evolve in the simple and uniform way that Morgan supposed, Morgan's study of kinship started a whole new branch of anthropology.

In the twentieth century, American anthropologists studied not only American Indians (whom they sometimes call "Amerinds") but also primitive peoples in other parts of the world. They dug up, sorted, classified, and described human remains and artifacts. They helped their colleagues in other lands to unravel the puzzle of man's origin and the development of his many cultures and civilizations. They even learned to look upon their own modern American culture with the detached, skeptical eye of an outsider.

The two outstanding figures in American anthropology of this time were the German-born Franz Boas (1858–1942) and the Czech-born Aleš Hrdlička [1] (1869–1943). Boas, a professor at Columbia University for forty-one years, collected data on the Eskimos and the Indians of the west coast of Canada. He had vast influence on his students because of his forceful personality. A careful collector of data rather than a theorizer, he refrained from sweeping statements about the origin and nature of man.

Hrdlička, working at the National Museum in Washington, studied the development of man's body. He examined bones and skulls from all over the world and settled the question of the origin of the American Indians.

Although it was guessed as long ago as the seventeenth century that American Indians came from Asia by way of Siberia, men long continued to speculate about their being of Welsh, Jewish, Egyptian, or Negro origin. Some even supposed that they came from a now sunken continent in the Atlantic, although no such continent ever existed. Hrdlička's researches made it clear that the American Indians had migrated from Asia across the Bering Strait and down the west coast of America over ten thousand years ago.

In the twentieth century, women began entering the field of anthropology. They found that they would often be accepted by the primitive tribes with whom they went to live; whereas strange white men were looked upon with suspicion by the male leaders of the tribe. One of the best-known women anthropologists in the field today is Margaret Mead. She has been a member of several expeditions to the Pacific and has done notable research in New Guinea, Samoa, and Bali. She has compared children brought up in these cultures with young Americans and has made a number of interesting observations on the effect of our way of life on the personalities of the next generation of Americans.

It is well that anthropologists went to work a century ago to investigate primitive peoples; for nowadays airplane travel and television sets are busily at work bringing modern Western civilization to primitive peoples in the most remote areas of the globe. Within the lifetime of people now living, perhaps, the differences that have made it possible to gain an idea of the way our ancestors lived in earlier societies will have vanished. It may be that, in another half-century, a traveler will travel the whole world over and never see costumes, customs, and cultures very different from those he is familiar with at home.

Side by side with the study of primitive man, scientists a century ago became interested in discovering every possible clue to the mysteries of the past. Searching for and studying man's tools, weapons, writings, roads, and buildings is the work of archaeologists. Archaeology is a new science; until a century ago, the techniques of unearthing, preserving, and evaluating the relics of man had not been worked out. Now that the painstaking modern methods are well-known and the finds so intriguing, many high-school and college students are becoming amateur archaeologists.

The predecessor of the archaeologist was the antiquary, the man whose greatest pleasure in life was to find, collect, study, and report on the relics of former times. A few men took an interest in antique things as long as 2,500 years ago. Nabuna'id, the last Chaldean king of Babylon in the sixth century B.C., was an antiquary with a collection of Sumerian inscriptions, which were ancient even in his day. Most people, however, paid little heed to such matters until the Renaissance in Europe. In 1572, an English antiquarian society was formed and flourished until King James I abolished it for fear that its members might have political ambitions. Another such society appeared early in the eighteenth century; and antiquarian interests soon spread to other lands.

The methods of the antiquary make a modern archaeologist shudder, for much priceless evidence was ruined in the antiquary's awkward eagerness to dig out some handsome statue or vase for his collection. These early students of man's past were mainly interested in beautiful objects. They had no regard for stratigraphy—the study of the layers of earth or debris in which the find was lying. They occasionally tore up the ruins of a whole city to unearth one particular town, only to discover later that the city they had destroyed was the city they really sought. This happened to the famous and successful Heinrich Schliemann (1822–90). He dreamed of finding the Troy of the *Iliad;* but he dug right through the scanty remains of that city to an earlier Troy beneath it.

To an archaeologist, an archaeological site is what the scene of the crime is to a detective. To solve the problem—whether it be the lives of ancient men or the identity of a murderer—every little fact, no matter how trivial, must be noted before anything is moved. Once the site has been tampered with, the evidence is lost forever.

Still, antiquarianism was a stage through which the science of archaeology had to pass. At least the bungling antiquary, unlike most people of his time, was interested in the relics of the past; he did not view them as useless things to be melted down or broken up for present-day purposes.

The European colonists in America had their share of antiquaries who collected Indian relics as curios. Serious archaeology began with a New York lawyer, John Lloyd Stephens (1805–52), who rediscovered the ruined cities of the Mayan Indians in Central America. In the centuries since the Spaniards had smashed the Mayan civilization, these cities had become so overgrown by jungle that even learned men questioned whether fine Mayan cities had ever existed.

A short, lively, talkative bachelor with bushy red side-whiskers, Stephens traveled widely in the Old World in the 1830s, when the first Britons and Frenchmen were beginning to explore the relics of the past in the Near East. Besides visiting the main European capitals, Stephens made a perilous journey to the ruins of Petra in Arabia. He traveled from Cairo disguised as a Muslim merchant, while the shaykh who guided him enlivened the journey by demanding more money at every step.

In London, Stephens became friends with Frederick Catherwood, an English architectural draftsman who had likewise been traveling about the East in disguise, sketching old monuments at the risk of his life. When he returned to the United States, Stephens wrote a book on his Arabian journey. The book was praised by Edgar Allan Poe and became a best-seller.

Fascinated by vague and contradictory reports about the Central American ruins, Stephens arranged with Catherwood to visit the Mayan country and examine them. Stephens managed to get appointed U. S. Minister to the Federation of Central America, and the pair set out in 1839.

Stephens and Catherwood sailed to British Honduras and beat their way overland. On muleback, they wallowed through bottomless quagmires and jogged over hair-raising precipices. They narrowly escaped being shot by suspicious soldiers at Comitán on their way to the ruins of Copán. To the astonishment of the man who owned the land on which the ruins stood —for to him, the place was a useless patch of jungle—they paid fifty dollars for the whole site.

Leaving Catherwood camped at Copán to draw his pictures of the ruins, Stephens went off to find the central government. He was almost eaten alive by mosquitoes, fleas, and ticks. He shivered and sweltered in the throes of malaria. He was drenched by tropical thunderstorms, shaken by an earthquake, and singed by a forest fire. He peered into the craters of erupting volcanoes, avoided an ambush by bandits, and helped to subdue an American sea captain taken with a fit. Then, at the end of his journey, he discovered that the Federation of Central America, in the throes of revolution, was about to break up into five separate republics.

When the Federation finally collapsed, Stephens packed the American Embassy's effects and went back to archaeology. He and Catherwood made their way to Palenque in Yucatán over a terrifying trail that wound up and down over cliffs and jungles. At Palenque, they sweated to clear away the forest and sketch the ruins until they were felled by disease and insect bites. They repeated their labors at Uxmal and then returned to New York.

A MAYAN TEMPLE PYRAMID IN YUCATAN

Back home, Stephens wrote his most successful book: *Incidents of Travel in Central America, Chiapas, and Yucatan,* one of the world's most exciting travel tales. Stephens insisted that the Mayan cities had been built, not as some thought by colonists from Egypt or some other Old World nation, but by the same short, brown, slant-eyed people who still farmed the flat plain of Yucatán. In this opinion, Stephens proved to be right. He and Catherwood made another journey to Central America and discovered the remains of the Mayan road system. After more books and further travel, both men worked at railroading in Latin America until Stephens succumbed to malaria and Catherwood perished in a shipwreck.

During the nineteenth century, the Near East was a favorite scene of archaeological exploration. Many people could be persuaded to give money for expeditions to that part of the world in the hope that new discoveries might shed further light on the Bible.

In the 1880s, an Episcopal clergyman, John Punnett Peters (1852–1921), obtained money from a group of Philadelphia capitalists for a series of expeditions to the site of the Babylonian city of Nippur, in central Iraq. The first full expedition, which set out in 1888, failed because the party became involved with an intertribal war among the local Arabs, some of whom burned down the American camp and looted it.

Three later expeditions were more successful, despite a fierce feud that sprang up among the explorers themselves. On one side were the leaders of the expedition: Peters and the archaeologist John Henry Haynes (1849–1910). On the other was the able, aggressive, and overbearing German-American Assyriologist, Hermann Volrath Hilprecht (1859–1925), the scientific director of the group.

Hilprecht insisted on the new method of archaeological digging. According to this method, the whole site is peeled off, layer by layer; and a careful record is kept of the original location of every brick and stone. Peters and Haynes, on the other hand, used the primitive methods of the earlier archaeologists, methods that were little better than treasure-hunting and that netted the scientists far less information than the newer system.

The quarrel continued, with public charges and inquiries, after the diggers had returned for the last time to the United States. Peters accused Hilprecht of faking the pictures in his books about the expedition and of keeping some of the expedition's finds for himself. A committee from the University of Pennsylvania investigated and cleared Hilprecht of the charges. Haynes went permanently insane. Criticism of Hilprecht by his colleagues at last drove him to resign his post at the University and go back to Germany. After the First World War, he returned to the United States to spend his last years here.

Despite these upheavals, the expedition gathered a vast mass of information and thousands of tablets inscribed in cuneiform writing. Cuneiform writing, which looks like the tracks of little birds, was pressed into wet clay tablets with the tips of reeds by the people of ancient Iraq. Scholars have been working on these tablets ever since the expedition, deciphering them and publishing the results.

Since then, American archaeological expeditions have dug at many sites in the Old World and the New. In 1899, Howard Crosby Butler (1872–1922) began his excavations in Syria. He made himself so well liked and trusted that in 1909 the Turkish government invited him to excavate the ruins of Sardis, the capital of ancient Lydia, a job which he undertook in 1910 and 1922. James Harvey Breasted (1865–1935), of the University of Chicago, began his famous Egyptian investigations in 1905. The American School of Archeology in Greece set up long-term programs of excavation and restoration at Corinth and Athens.

From 1922 to 1934, the University of Pennsylvania took part

in a joint Anglo-American expedition to the site of the ancient Sumerian city of Ur, in southern Iraq. The leader of the expedition was Sir Leonard Woolley (1880–1960), who had previously dug in Britain, Nubia, and Turkey. His second in command was Leon Legrain, a French Catholic priest who worked for the University Museum at the University of Pennsylvania for nearly thirty years.

This expedition to Ur resulted in some spectacular discoveries. Among these were the graves of King Abargi and Queen Shubad, who reigned in Ur about 2500 B.C. The graves contained not only the skeletons of the king and queen but also those of about ninety ladies' maids, musicians, soldiers, and other court attendants, who had been sacrificed and buried with the royal couple to continue to serve them in the next world.

The University of Pennsylvania also sponsored major archaeological expeditions in the New World. The largest of all the Mayan cities was Tikal, buried in the jungle of northern Guatemala. Abandoned since about the year 900, Tikal became gradually known to the outside world because of a series of expeditions sent out from various nations. In the 1880s a Briton, Alfred P. Maudslay, who undertook seven expeditions to Central America, had casts made of the carvings on Mayan monuments for the Victoria and Alfred Museum. Teobert Maler, an Austrian working for the Peabody Museum of Harvard, had unearthed and measured various buildings at Tikal in 1895 and 1904. But, as a result of a quarrel between Maler and his museum, his report remained unfinished until Alfred M. Tozzer completed it in 1910.

After the Second World War, archaeologists of the University Museum of the University of Pennsylvania laid plans for a long-range program of clearing, excavation, and restoration of Tikal. Money for this work came from a number of sources, including the Rockefeller and Carnegie Foundations. The Guatemalan government became interested, declared the area a national park, and furnished the archaeologists with free air-freight service between the site and Guatemala City.

Most of the excavation to date has been done in the center of the city, the one-acre Plaza Mayor, or "main square." When Tikal was a thriving metropolis with many thousands of inhabitants, this plaza was completely paved and surrounded on all sides by towering buildings, including two great pyramids, about ten stories high, at the top of which were temples to the gods.

Other stone structures stretch out beneath the encroaching jungle for two or three miles in all directions. In the days of its greatness, Tikal must have had about forty large and two hundred smaller public buildings. Thousands of huts, made of wood and thatch, undoubtedly huddled in the smaller streets beyond the wide public squares and ceremonial roads; but of these homes of the common people, nothing today remains.

Several important American universities organize archaeological expeditions every year. The University of Pennsylvania continues to be one of the most faithful in its efforts to increase man's knowledge of his past. As of this writing, it has equipped one of its younger archaeologists, George Bass, with the first midget submarine for under-water archaeological exploration. He and his assistants spent the summer of 1965 off the coast of Greece locating and studying the wrecks of ancient ships that broke up on the rocky headlands of that bleak shore. The shape of the ships, the kind of cargo they carried, the coins that went down with the sailors that might indicate the period of the wreck—all these and much besides will add immeasurably to our understanding of the early peoples of the Mediterranean Sea.

The American contribution to the science of archaeology that will probably prove our greatest contribution in the long run is neither the finding of an important ruin nor the decipherment of an ancient script. It is a discovery, made by the physicist Willard F. Libby of the University of Chicago, of a new and more effective method of measuring the age of the relics of early men. The earlier archaeologists struggled to find reliable ways of telling the age of prehistoric ruins and remains by estimating the rate at which glaciers advance and retreat, or the rate at which peat bogs are formed, or by counting the rings in logs used in buildings and comparing them with stumps of trees.

Libby's method, called radiocarbon dating and worked out between 1945 and 1950, depends upon radioactivity. Scientists had already found out that most elements occur in several variations, called isotopes, which behave exactly alike chemically but which have atoms of different weights. For example, carbon (of which "C" is the chemical symbol) comes in three isotopes: C-12, C-13, and C-14. They are so named because their atoms weigh about twelve, thirteen, and fourteen times as much as a hydrogen atom.

Libby discovered that, of the carbon in the atmosphere and in living creatures, about 99 per cent is C-12, one per cent is C-13, and a microscopically small amount is C-14. Whereas the atoms of C-12 and C-13 remain the same from age to age, those of C-14 are radioactive. That is, they break down into nitrogen atoms in accordance with a regular rule. Of every radioactive carbon atom (C-14), half will turn into nitrogen in 5,568 years; half the remainder will break down in the next 5,568 years, and so on.

Now, any living thing, while eating and breathing, absorbs carbon and gives it out again. Therefore, while it lives, the proportion of C-14 in its body remains the same as that in the world around it. When the plant or animal dies, however, it stops absorbing carbon from the outside world, while the C-14 in its body continues to change back into nitrogen. Thus after 5,568 years, there will be only half as much C-14 in the body as there was when the creature died. After 11,136 years, there will only be a quarter as much. Therefore, by measuring the proportion of C-14 in relics that contain carbon, such as a bit of a mummy, or a sea shell, or charcoal from a campfire, we can tell just how long ago that person, that shell, or that tree was alive.

Since 1950, great numbers of articles from archaeological sites have been checked in this way. Often the age measurements confirmed what was already known from other data; but some of the measurements gave the scientists big surprises. The last retreat of the ice in the Pleistocene Period, for instance, turns out to have been much more recent than was formerly thought—a mere 11,000 years ago. Later scientists have developed more advanced methods of radiocarbon dating so that measurements can be made even more accurately and can cover a longer span of time.

Thus American science has unlocked one more door to the secrets of the past and has given us new glimpses of the world as it appeared to our ancestors. Since the science of archaeology is growing fast, and since the people and governments of many nations are rapidly becoming interested in encouraging the discovery and preservation of their national relics, future generations may learn many new and fascinating things about the people who quarreled and traded and loved and danced in cities built thousands of years ago.

In 1837, the French philosopher Auguste Comte (1798–1857) suggested that there ought to be a science called "sociology," to make some order out of the many scraps of information then known about human societies. Nobody paid much attention to this suggestion until thirty years later, when the English philosopher Herbert Spencer (1820–1903) set forth what he considered the scientific principles of sociology. Spencer was interested in the subject of evolution even before Darwin published his *Origin of Species*. Spencer eagerly embraced Darwin's theories, popularized the word "evolution," and coined the phrase "survival of the fittest."

Spencer believed that human individuals, communities, and nations evolved because they competed in a constant, ferocious "struggle for survival," just as wild species do. He assumed that it was natural for the weaker individuals to be destroyed. These arguments furnished justification to anybody who wanted to oppress the poor, exploit his neighbor, or attack a foreign nation.

Human societies do evolve, of course; but they evolve according to laws quite different from those governing the creatures of the wild. For one thing, the life cycle of a society is measured in mere centuries, while that of a species runs to hundreds of thousands of years. Moreover, in the development of a society, coöperation is quite as important as competition. Therefore, while Spencer deserves the credit for founding the science of sociology, most of his theories have long since been discarded.

The new science of sociology soon reached America, and the American Sociological Society was formed in 1905. One of the early American sociologists was William Graham Sumner (1840–1910), a professor at Yale. Sumner agreed with Spencer that human progress depended on the "survival of the fittest" and that the untrained, the sick, and the poor should be allowed to die unaided. He feared that the tendency of governments and private charities to help "unfit" persons to survive would bring human progress to a halt.

However, most of the early American sociologists held quite a different point of view. Most of them were country-bred; many were sons of preachers. They believed that sociology was a tool by which man's lot on earth might be improved. Since our nation was at that time growing rapidly richer and our standards of living were rising, these sociologists sought to improve the lot of the less fortunate and so help this process along.

In the early days of sociology, many men tried to explain the behavior of man by saying that his actions were guided by instincts. Later, the psychologists studied human behavior more closely and found that man differs from all other animals not only in his greater intelligence but also in his almost complete lack of true instincts. Unlike the spiders, which are born with a knowledge of web-building, or the birds, which can always make nests just like that of all other birds of their species, man has hardly any automatic, built-in controls to direct his actions.

Because man has hardly any instinctual behavior, he can modify his actions more readily than can the other animals. In other words, he is more teachable. Lester F. Ward (1841–1913) realized that, at least to some extent, man lacked instincts. He classified universal human tendencies into a number of "social forces," such as the tendency to avoid pain, to defend one's family, and to keep the respect of one's fellow men.

The First World War gave the kindly sociologists who thought of man as a reasoning creature quite a jolt. They discovered that civilized man was not altogether dedicated to peaceful progress; but that, instead, he was an emotional being, well-supplied with destructive and irrational urges. One man who had few illusions about the human race was Thorstein [2] Veblen (1857–1929). Born of Norwegian parents in Wisconsin, Veblen spent his life as a professor of economics at various American universities. Although he is classed as an economist, his most influential work, *The Theory of the Leisure Class* (1899), was more a treatise on sociology than on economics.

Veblen was a strange man. Although he was tall and had a sturdy build, he affected an air of sad, weary helplessness. He liked to play cruel little practical jokes on people and was often in hot water over love affairs with the wives of other professors. He lectured in a mumbling monotone which discouraged all but the hardiest students, and wrote in a style salted with long, learned words and peppered with biting, ironic humor. He was a poor economist because he never mastered statistics. Still, his theories achieved great popularity in the bleak years of the

Great Depression that followed the stock market crash of 1929.

Veblen's theory of the leisure class is this: when people have more income than they need to keep alive, they spend the surplus, not in improving themselves or even in adding to their comforts and conveniences, but in trying to impress others with the fact that they are rich. They do things they do not even enjoy just to prove to any onlooker that they are above vulgar toil. This activity, which Veblen called "conspicuous consumption," may involve inconvenience, discomfort, and even physical suffering. For example, in old China, the daughters of upper-class families always had their feet bound so that they could not grow normally. By forcing his womenfolk to totter around on tiny, deformed feet, the Chinese gentleman proved to the world that his women did no work, since obviously they were unable to do so. At the turn of the present century, American and European women achieved a somewhat similar effect by wearing corsets so tight that they would faint after any effort or emotional strain.

Conspicuous consumption can even take the form of deliberate waste. One example of this is the enormous dinners that were formerly served in expensive restaurants or in the homes of millionaires. The most notable extravagance of this kind was found among the American Indians of certain northwestern tribes. From time to time, rich Indians planned parties called "potlatches," at which they gave away or destroyed all their worldly goods—furs, boats, slaves, and the like—just to show their neighbors their contempt for wealth.

Of course, Veblen was writing about conditions in the 1890s, when wealthy Americans as a matter of course gave enormous balls, owned private railroad cars, maintained mansions both in New York and Newport, and otherwise put their wealth on public display. Nevertheless, conspicuous consumption and conspicuous waste are still a part of the general American way of life. If one looks around today, one sees enough examples of waste of time, effort, and wealth in mere showing off, to prove that at least some people still deserve Veblen's acid criticism.

After the First World War, the study of sociology increased in American colleges and universities. American sociologists spent less time in theory and more in digging up facts about the way various people tended to live. In 1924 and 1925, Robert S. Lynd and his wife Helen studied the town of Muncie, Indiana, under the alias of "Middletown." Settling into the neighborhood, they investigated what the people did day by day, what social customs they practiced, and what beliefs they held. They examined the people as if they had never seen a Midwestern American town before. Their findings gave their readers an astonishingly clear picture of twentieth-century city life and its effect on the individual.

As a result of the Great Depression and the following Second World War, sociologists were drawn into government service and given a chance to put into action some of their theories for improving the lot of mankind. Out of this effort came social security plans, child-welfare agencies, pre-kindergarten training programs, and free medical care for the aged. Robert E. Park told people that most men work hard to maintain their "social status"; while William F. Ogburn noted that there is a considerable "cultural lag" in a fast-changing society like America's because many cling to the ideas they learned when they were young, even though these ideas have become obsolete.

Since the 1910s, when large numbers of young women first began to go out to work in offices and factories, social patterns have been undergoing enormous changes. Customs in common use even twenty years ago seem "square" to today's teenagers.

Today, in many American universities, sociologists are trying to find out why crime is on the increase in urban areas and why younger children are getting involved in a growing number of serious crimes. They are considering the rise in drug addiction and how to control it. They are wondering how to make the center of our cities over into neighborhoods where middle-class people will once again want to bring up their families. They are comparing America with the civilizations of Greece and Rome and wondering if our civilization, for all its material wealth, is on the decline.

It may be observed that anthropology and sociology are not exact sciences. It is not possible to do scientific experiments with two children, two towns, or two nations. Comparisons can only be made where two opposed conditions already exist. Because of this, we cannot expect from sociology discoveries as dramatic as those of the archaeologists, nor inventions as world-shaking as the atomic bomb. However, we are slowly learning how our mechanized civilization affects the individual and the larger groups of which he is a part. We are finding out how to counteract some of the dangers inherent in big city life in this age of swift cars, swifter rockets, and rapidly changing standards of behavior.

PART FOUR
The Applied Sciences

XIV · THE ELECTRICAL REVOLUTION

One cold, wet day in March, 1875, an inventor from Boston came to the Smithsonian Institution to talk to Joseph Henry. The visitor, a tall, slim, polite, shabby young Scot, with bushy black hair and long droopy sidewhiskers, was Alexander Graham Bell (1847–1922). A teacher of speech to the deaf-mutes, he had been trying to send spoken words over wires. Henry said:

"You have the germ of a great invention. Work at it."

Bell complained: "But I have not the electrical knowledge necessary to overcome the difficulties!"

"Get it," said Henry, no man to waste words.[1]

Bell got it. In June, when Bell and his assistant Thomas A. Watson (1854–1934) were experimenting with a sound-transmitting apparatus, two parts accidentally became over-heated and welded together, so that the apparatus transmitted a musical note. Ten more months of hard work followed. On March 10, 1876, while working downstairs, Watson heard Bell, who had just spilled acid on his trousers, say over the machine:

"Mr. Watson, please come here; I want you."

Watson bounded up the stairs, crying: "I can hear you! I can hear the *words!*"

Later, Watson remarked: "Perhaps if Mr. Bell had realized

that he was about to make a bit of history, he would have prepared a more sounding and interesting sentence." [2]

In May, 1876, President Grant and Emperor Pedro II of Brazil opened the Philadelphia Centennial Exposition in Fairmount Park. This exposition showed the world that the United States was fast overtaking Germany as the leading nation in engineering and invention.

In Machinery Hall, amid a hideous din, a huge steam engine drove scores of other machines by means of a multitude of slapping belts. Here stood two small exhibits, the dynamo or electric generator of the Belgian inventor Zénobe Théophile Gramme (1826–1901) and Bell's telephone. Neither received much attention until June 25th, the day that the judges, headed by Joseph Henry and accompanied by Emperor Pedro, were to select the prize-winning exhibits.

The sweltering judges had reached Bell's exhibit when they decided to call it a day. One picked up the telephone receiver, looked at it blankly, and put it down. Another made a small joke at Bell's expense. At that moment, the burly emperor recognized Bell, whom he had met before. He strode over, beaming through his square, blond beard and saying:

"How do you do, Meester Bell? And how are the deaf-mutes in Boston?"

Bell answered that he was sorry the judges could not inspect his invention until the next day, because he had to return to Boston to give an examination at the School for the Deaf.

"Ah!" said Dom Pedro. "Then we must look at it now."

Soon the judges were delightedly reciting Shakespeare to each other by telephone. His monocle gleaming, Sir William Thomson (1824–1907), the British physicist who had done much to make the Atlantic cable practical, cried: "This is the most wonderful thing I have seen in America!" [3]

Bell's patent application reached the Patent Office only a few hours before that of an unlucky rival telephone inventor,

Elisha Gray (1835–1901). Because of this, when the telephone went into use, Bell won about 600 patent-infringement suits and sold his stock in the Bell Telephone Company for a fortune.

In later years Bell, a man of great push and enthusiasm, became active in various scientific organizations, to which he gave generously. He also founded the magazine *Science,* the publication of the American Association for the Advancement of Science.

By the time of the Columbian Exposition of 1893, held in Chicago, the effects of the electrical revolution were plain to see. Gone was the forest of flapping belts, their place taken by quiet little electric motors. The fair grounds were lit by electric lights; telephones and electric streetcars were becoming common.

The scientific discoveries on which this electrical revolution were based had been mostly made in Britain and Germany, by Michael Faraday, James Clerk Maxwell, William Thomson, Hermann von Helmholz, and Heinrich R. Hertz. Electric motors and generators were developed by many inventors, both in America and in Europe. The electric arc light was invented by the British chemist Sir Humphry Davy (1778–1829) in the early 1800s and made practical in the 1870s by Pavel Yablochkov, a Russian engineer working in France, and by the electrician Charles F. Brush (1849–1929) in the United States.

The electric arc light is fine for street lighting but gives too bright a glare for household use. If one lowers the voltage, the light does not dim; it goes out. A generation of inventors struggled with the problem of "subdivision of the electric light," to make home lighting possible.

The man who succeeded was Thomas Alva Edison (1847–1931), one of the most inventive men of all time. Edison's father was a dealer in feed, grain, and lumber, and Edison's boyhood was spent in Port Huron, at the eastern tip of Michigan. Edison left school after only three months. He later explained that the teacher complained to his mother that he was "addled," meaning that he asked too many questions. A likelier reason is that his father could not afford the school fees. In any case, Edison's mother, a former teacher, gave him an adequate elementary education at home. After an attack of scarlet fever, his hearing decreased little by little, until as a mature man he could scarcely hear words shouted in his ear.

Edison soon acquired a passion for science and drove his parents to distraction by his experiments. He dripped sulfuric acid on the furniture until his chemicals were banished to the cellar.

As a youth, Edison worked as a wandering telegrapher, notably skilled but rather irresponsible. After several years of this life, he settled down as an engineer for a company that made stock tickers. After the Western Union Company bought up the stock-ticker company, Edison continued to invent devices for Western Union as a free-lance inventor without any definite contract. At last General Marshall Lefferts, the president of Western Union, called Edison in and asked how much he thought the company should pay him for the rights to his inventions.

Edison had no idea. He thought of asking for $5,000 and accepting $3,000. In desperation he said: "Well, General, suppose you make me an offer." [4]

"How would forty thousand dollars strike you?"

Edison came "as near to fainting as I ever got," but managed to say yes. Three days later, he signed the contract and received the first check he had ever handled. When he asked for cash at the bank, the teller thought it would be a good joke to give Edison his forty thousand in small bills. Edison sat up all night guarding his huge wad, until next day Lefferts showed him how to open a bank account.

With this money, Edison opened a strange sort of shop in

Newark. This was a commercial laboratory whose product was inventions. As he knew nothing about bookkeeping, he ran his shop in what seemed an eccentric manner. Nevertheless, he developed an automatic telegraph and new kinds of telegraph for sending as many as four messages over the same wire at once. He also invented waxed wrapping paper, the electric pen (a device for cutting stencils in longhand), and the mimeograph machine. He was taking out a patent a month.

In 1876, Edison bought an estate at Menlo Park, New Jersey. In his thirties, he was a solidly built man, clean-shaven in a bearded age, with thick, dark, graying hair. His manner was pleasant but aloof. As with Newton and Gibbs, his mind was so full of technical ideas that he had but little interest in human affairs and little time for people.

At Menlo Park, Edison invented many things. Of these, the most important were the carbon telephone transmitter, the phonograph, and the electric light. With the carbon transmitter, one could talk over the telephone without shouting.

While Edison was working on telephones, he noticed that a telegraphic repeater with which he had been experimenting gave forth speechlike sounds when its disks turned rapidly. This gave him the idea that speech sounds, as well as the clicks and buzzes of telegraphic signals, could be permanently recorded and played back.

After several months of quiet experiment, Edison handed a sketch to John Kreusi, his Swiss assistant. The apparatus, he said, ought not to cost more than eighteen dollars. Kreusi was astonished when Edison told him what it was for. Carman, the foreman of the machine shop, bet Edison a box of cigars that it would not work.

When finished, the machine looked like a little hand lathe. It had a shaft with a handle at one end, a flywheel at the other, and a tinfoil-wrapped cylinder between. A guide carried a device with a diaphragm and a needle. As the handle was turned, the gadget moved slowly along the guide and the needle scratched a groove in the cylinder. When the contraption was ready, Edison turned the handle and shouted at the gadget with the needle:

"Mary had a little lamb.
Its fleece was white as snow!"

Edison returned the machine to its starting position and turned the crank again. The machine squeaked:

Mary had a little lamb.
Its fleece was white as snow.

Carmen paid his cigars, and Edison named his new device the phonograph. He obtained his patent almost without argument. The Patent Office examiner had not found a single patent on a similar device, a rare thing in our inventive age.

Then Edison attacked the problem of subdividing the electric light. This is a more typical tale of modern invention. It is a story of many brilliant men racing for the same goal, with one arriving a little ahead of the rest.

Inventors had long experimented with incandescent lights made of platinum wires or carbon rods, but none of these lights burned long enough to be practical. Edison worked for a while with platinum wires but found that platinum melts at a temperature only a few degrees above that at which it glows. Therefore a very slight overload melts the wire.

Then Edison did some hard thinking and calculating. He decided that the only thing that would serve was a thin filament of *carbon*. The earlier inventors had used thick carbon rods or metal wires. To make such lamps glow, large currents requiring huge amounts of costly copper would be needed. Edison, on the other hand, saw that to use a very thin filament would make a lamp bulb of high electrical *resistance*. Since a given *voltage* (that is, electrical pressure) would send much less current through such a lamp, he would have to use a higher voltage to get the same amount of power. (With direct current, power is the product of the voltage and the *amperage*, the amount of electric current.) By using a higher voltage and a lower amperage, the power wires could be made much thinner and cheaper.

But how to find carbon as slender as a thread, which would not only carry the current but would keep its shape despite rough usage? The ordinary forms that carbon takes—soot, coal, graphite, and diamond—are not in the least threadlike. Edison finally induced a lamp containing a cotton thread, baked until it was almost entirely carbonized, to glow for forty hours; but this filament was so fragile that the slightest jar would have shattered it.

Thereafter, Edison tried carbonizing a number of substances, including bagging, wood shavings, celluloid, coconut fiber, cork, fishing line, flax, lampwick, tissue paper, twine, and some hairs from the beard of his old friend Mackenzie, who had taught him telegraphy. He had the best luck with Bristol cardboard, from which he made some of his first commercial lamps. Later, bamboo fiber proved even better and remained the standard incandescent-bulb filament for several years. Finally, other materials took its place. Now we use the tungsten filament invented by the American physicist William D. Coolidge (b.1873).

With the financial backing of the famous banker, J. Pierpont Morgan, Edison made and sold his light bulbs and developed electrical power systems to use them. Although he is best remembered for the electric light, he actually showed more originality in devising a generating and distributing system to furnish these lamps with electric current. He used steam engines to generate electric current.

The first Edison generating station went into service in London, on January 12, 1882. The following September, the plant on Pearl Street, New York, started up. During one test run, a leak in the power mains set the horses on Fulton Street to dancing because their hoofs tingled. On a later occasion, there was trouble with the speed regulators; some engines stopped while others raced. The crew fled, leaving Edison and one brave engineer to shut off the steam.

There are two kinds of electric current: direct current, which flows in one direction only, and alternating current, which flows through the wires first one way and then the other. Ordinary house current is sixty-cycle alternating current, which changes its direction back and forth sixty times a second. Edison worked exclusively with direct current. This type of current has advantages. For one thing, direct-current machinery can easily be varied in speed; therefore, direct current is commonly used to drive things like subway trains and elevators.

However, alternating current also has certain advantages. The alternating-current generator is simpler. Moreover, alternating current can be sent over long distances more cheaply than direct current. This is done by a device called a *transformer*, which raises the voltage, or electrical pressure in the line, while lowering the amperage, or amount of current flowing.

The man who did the most to develop alternating-current power systems was Elihu Thomson (1853–1937). Born in England and reared in Philadelphia, Thomson was a small, slight, talkative man with a large mustache in a thin, square-jawed face. His many inventions included arc welding, the De Laval cream separator, and the high-frequency dynamo.

In the 1880s, Thomson's backers set him up in a laboratory in Lynn, Massachusetts. Here he improved the transformer (newly invented by L. Gaulard and J. D. Gibbs in Europe) and developed a system for generating and sending out alternating-current power, just as Edison had done for direct-current power.

To protect houses, in the rare case that the high-voltage current in the main wires should leak through the transformer into the household wires, Thomson invented a system of grounding the coil that fed the household circuit. If you look in your fuse box, you will see a wire coming out of the transformer casing and clamped to a water pipe. This is Thomson's invention.

Edison's company fought Thomson's company with lawsuits and pamphlets. Despite the bitter rivalry between their companies, Thomson and Edison were good friends. While Edison, with over a thousand patents to his name, was the most productive inventor in the nation's history, Thomson, with 692, was the second most productive.

Moreover, while Edison was a pure inventor and little else, Thomson was a better-rounded man. He was not only a supreme inventor but also a brilliant research scientist, an effective teacher and lecturer, an expert patent attorney, and a keen businessman.

After the Battle of the Currents had raged for years, J. P. Morgan arranged a merger between the companies of Thomson and Edison. The new company became today's General Electric Company. Mindful of the continuing need for improvements, in 1900, General Electric started a department for independent research—the first such department in any American company.

In his later years, Edison invented the alkaline storage battery, magnetic mining machinery, and (with an assistant named William K. L. Dickson) one early type of motion-picture camera. Although the majority of motion-picture cameras and projectors were developed by French inventors, Edison deserves much credit for devising methods of filming action and the entire credit for producing the first sound motion picture.

Although he had one of the most inventive minds of all time, Thomas Edison was not always scrupulous. Sometimes he allowed his admirers to credit him with inventions with which he had little or nothing to do. When he lost much of his fortune in an iron-mining venture in New Jersey, he regained his losses by buying up several other inventors' patents and thus seizing control of the infant motion-picture industry. However, in 1917, the courts declared that Edison's control of the industry violated the antitrust laws; and Edison's company was broken up.

Several inventors and engineers who played leading parts in the electrical revolution worked for Edison at one time or another. One, for instance, was Frank Julian Sprague (1857–1934), who invented the electric elevator and was one of the inventors of railway electrification. Among Sprague's inventions was multiple-unit control, by which the motorman of a subway train controls the motors in all the cars at once.

Another inventor, a tall, thin, devilish-looking man named Nikola Tesla (1857–1943), came to America from Croatia in the Balkans. Tesla's great invention was the induction motor, in which there is no direct connection between the armature or rotor (the turning part) and the electric circuit. The induction motor, in which the magnetic field of the motor spins round and round, dragging the rotor with it, is one of the most important types of motor, especially for factory machinery.

A touchy eccentric, Tesla was always quitting his job because he thought himself wronged or insulted. Thus he left Edison in anger and later left Westinghouse Electric Company, which had bought the rights to his induction motor.

For years, Tesla was very productive. He invented generators, transformers, condensers, and other electrical machinery. But he ran his affairs in a wildly unbusinesslike manner, and after 1905 his inventiveness dried up. For the last thirty years of his life, he was an eminent crank. Every year he promised amazing inventions, such as a death ray or communication with other planets, but none of these marvels ever came into being.

Another of Edison's onetime employees was Reginald Aubrey Fessenden (1866–1932), a big, bearded Canadian.

While working as a tester and inspector for Edison, Fessenden —headstrong, impatient, lavish with his backers' money, and a nonstop talker—devised the modern method of encasing household electric wires in galvanized-iron pipe to reduce the risk of setting the house afire. After making several distinguished inventions, Fessenden attacked the problem of sending sounds through space.

Wireless telegraphy had been made practical by an Italian inventor, Guglielmo Marconi (1874–1937). In the complex story of wireless telegraphy, Marconi was the most important single inventor. He combined a detecting device called a *coherer* (invented by Edouard Branly in France) with an antenna or aerial (invented by Aleksandr S. Popov in Russia). By Marconi's wireless system, one could transmit the buzzes and clicks of the Morse code. With each passing year, Marconi sent his messages over longer and longer distances. By 1899, two American battleships, using his apparatus, were speaking to each other at a distance of 36 miles. In that same year, Marconi's invention saved the crew of a lightship anchored near the treacherous Goodwin Sands, off the southeast coast of England, when a freighter sank their ship.

Marconi's system had just come into use when his detector was made obsolete by Fessenden's "liquid barretter." Soon Fessenden persuaded two rich Pittsburghers to back him in developing wireless transmission of the sounds of speech. To convey the shape of sound waves through space, Fessenden obtained a generator that put out an alternating current of a steady high frequency, generating a larger number of electromagnetic waves per second. The size of the waves, however, was changeable. It was made greater or smaller in proportion to the rise and fall of the much slower sound waves. To receive the message, a detector picked up the electromagnetic waves flying through space and turned them back into sound waves.

On Christmas Eve, 1906, Fessenden put on the world's first radio broadcast. The owners of Fessenden's wireless apparatus, which had been rattling out the clicks and buzzes of the Morse code, were surprised to hear voices and music issuing from their sets. Fessenden played his violin, and there were songs, speeches, and a poem.

Soon, however, Fessenden's company was wrecked by a quarrel between Fessenden and his backers. Meanwhile, another inventor, Lee De Forest (1873–1961), who had studied under Gibbs at Yale, invented a detector superior to Fessenden's barretter. This was the audion or triode vacuum tube.

The British electrical engineer, Sir John Ambrose Fleming (1849–1945), had devised an evacuated bulb (that is, one from which nearly all the air had been pumped) with two filaments, one hot and the other cold. Electrons would flow from the hot filament to the cold, but not the other way round. This was called the Edison effect, after an accidental discovery that Edison made but did not develop further. Hence the bulb acted as a one-way valve for electric current and turned alternating current into direct. Such an electrical valve is called a *rectifier*.

De Forest added a grid of wires between the two filaments. This addition made the device into a very sensitive detector. When the grid was joined to a radio aerial, and a voltage was applied between the two filaments, an incoming radio wave would cause a surge of current in the aerial and the grid. This surge of current choked off the flow of current between the filaments. Thus a very faint signal could be transformed into a very strong change of current. On this principle, the radio industry was built.

De Forest, like many other inventors, had a struggle. His original audion required much tinkering and refinement before it became practical. Moreover, in 1912, he and his backers were prosecuted for fraud on the ground that they were selling stock in a company to make a "worthless" device. The development of radio was further held up by the First World War, because the U. S. Government demanded that the experimenters stop work for fear that someone would radio information to the enemy.

In 1920, however, commercial broadcasting began in Pittsburgh and Detroit; and De Forest, who was always making a fortune one year and losing it the next, sold his audion rights to the American Telephone and Telegraph Company and went into the field of sound motion pictures.

The most important later advances in wireless communication were frequency modulation and television. Frequency modulation was developed by Edwin H. Armstrong (1890–1954), an early and bitterly hostile rival of De Forest. First, he developed the radio circuits called the superheterodyne and the superregenerative. Then, in the 1930s, he invented the frequency modulation system, which eliminates nearly all static.

Armstrong came to a pathetic end. Although rich in his later years, he became absorbed in lawsuits against several large companies that, he thought, had not paid what they owed him for the use of his inventions. These suits so preyed on his mind that he finally killed himself.

Television was developed by many engineers and inventors. Some of the basic work, such as the selenium photoelectric cell, goes back to the nineteenth century. One of the most important steps in the development of modern television was taken in 1923, when Charles Francis Jenkins (1867–1934) sent still pictures by wire for the first time. In this invention, the sending set "scans" the picture, sweeping its gaze over it and breaking it up into a series of narrow lines. The light and dark of each line are transformed into variations in electric current. At the other end, a device scans a photographic negative with a narrow beam of light, or scans the end of a television picture tube with a beam of electrons. The beam "paints" a copy of the original picture on the sensitive surface.

With Jenkins's original wirephoto apparatus, it took several minutes to send one picture. For television, the whole picture had to be scanned in a small fraction of a second. Hundreds of engineers, working for over a decade, finally produced experimental television in the 1930s. The art was ready for commercial use when the Second World War interrupted it; but television moved into American homes on a large scale at the end of that conflict.

Such, in brief, is the story of the great electrical revolution in the United States. During the early years of the twentieth century, progress was leisurely. Most electrical engineers devoted themselves to the improvement of motors, transformers, generators, relays, and other electrical machines of kinds already known. Then, in the 1930s, progress speeded up again with the development, not only of television, but also of radar and other devices.

At the Bell Telephone Laboratories, the physicist William Shockley pondered the shortcomings of De Forest's vacuum tube. Despite the vast numbers of these tubes needed for radios, the tube had limitations. It worked over a narrow band of frequencies only, and it wasted a lot of energy.

To get around these difficulties, Shockley and another Bell engineer, Walter H. Brattain, studied the neglected field of materials in the solid state. In particular, they studied the materials known as *semiconductors*. Most substances, like metals, are either very good conductors or, like glass and rubber, very poor conductors—so poor, in fact, that they can be used as insulators. There are, however, a few materials halfway between the conductors and the nonconductors. These are crystals of elements like silicon and germanium with a trace of impurities.

Sometimes each atom of the impurity has one more electron than the material needs, simply to enable the atom to fit into the crystal structure. When an electrical force is applied to such a crystal, the extra electrons move about in it. When each atom of the impurity has one *less* electron than is needed by the crystal structure, the electrons also move—but into the vacant places provided by the impurities. As each atom captures

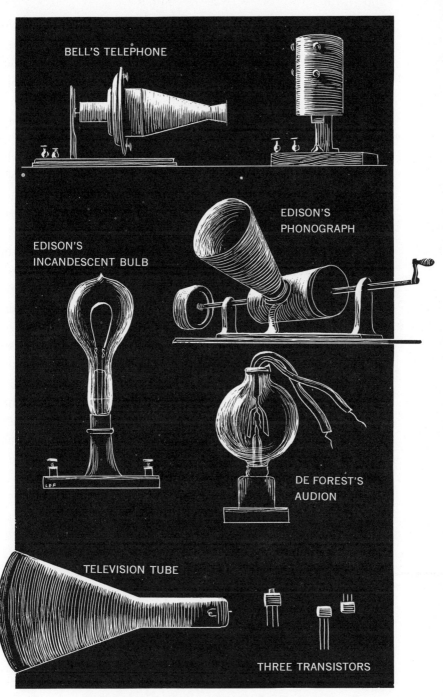

BELL'S TELEPHONE

EDISON'S PHONOGRAPH

EDISON'S INCANDESCENT BULB

DE FOREST'S AUDION

TELEVISION TUBE

THREE TRANSISTORS

INVENTIONS OF THE ELECTRICAL REVOLUTION

one of its neighbors' electrons, it is as if the "hole"—the gap in each atom's complement of electrons—were moving about. Materials of the first kind (in which extra electrons move about) are materials of n-type; of the second kind (in which positive "holes" move about) materials of p-type.

Work on the solid-state amplifier was halted by the Second World War. Afterward, with John Bardeen as a new member of the Bell Laboratories group and Shockley as supervisor, the team took up its work again. They found that, with a sandwich-like structure composed of a slice of p-type material between two pieces of n-type, or a piece of n-type between two of p-type, they could make an amplifier or electrical valve called a transistor. This device proved as effective as a vacuum tube in many cases, while it was much smaller, more rugged, and more durable. As with the vacuum tube, a small variation in the input voltage brought about a much larger variation in the output.

In 1956, Shockley, Brattain, and Bardeen shared the Nobel Prize in physics for their work. Since then, transistors of many kinds have been developed. Radios have been reduced to a fraction of their former size, and the electrical revolution has proceeded to the invention of wholly new devices like masers and lasers. Men in the coming century will see uses for electrical apparatus that have not yet even been imagined.

XV · THE INTERNAL-COMBUSTION REVOLUTION

Following closely upon the electrical revolution came another great change in American life, brought about by the internal-combustion engine. In such engines, the fuel is not burned outside the engine to boil water, as in the steam engine. It is burned inside the engine itself, and the expansion of hot gases furnishes the power.

The first internal-combustion engine that worked at all well was made in France, in 1860, by Étienne Lenoir (1822–1900). The Lenoir engine did not actually burn the fuel inside the cylinder. Instead, it worked on a principle like that of Ericson's hot-air engine, which was also popular at this time. Liquid fuel was burned outside the cylinder, and the hot gases from this combustion were let into the cylinder by a slide-valve mechanism as in a steam engine.

Although it ran smoothly enough, the Lenoir engine was very wasteful of fuel. Therefore, it gave way in the 1880s to engines of the *compression* type. In these, the fuel is mixed with air. Next, the mixture is drawn into the cylinder, compressed by the upstroke of the piston, and then exploded. The expansion of the gases drives the piston down and causes the crankshaft to turn.

The most successful engine of the compression type was that made in 1876 by the German engineer, Nikolaus August Otto

(1832–91). Otto's engine is called a four-stroke-cycle engine because, for every explosion in a cylinder, there are four strokes of the piston, two up and two down. On one downstroke, the piston sucks into the cylinder a mixture of fuel and air. On the following upstroke, the piston compresses the mixture. Then an electric spark explodes the mixture, driving the piston down. The fourth stroke of the piston pushes the burned gases out of the exhaust valve.

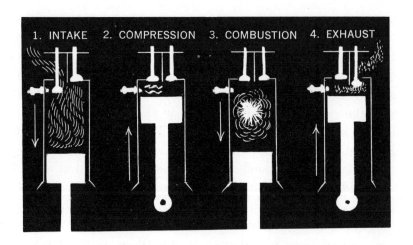

THE FOUR CYCLES OF THE OTTO ENGINE

The Otto engine proved at least twice as efficient, in economy of fuel, as the Lenoir engine. However, the early Otto engines were nothing like those we use today in our automobiles. Instead, they were big single-cylinder affairs, with massive flywheels, designed to furnish power for factories and the like. Moreover, they burned gas, not gasoline. Then another German engineer, Wilhelm Maybach (1847–1929), invented the carburetor, which made it possible to burn liquid fuels in an Otto engine. The carburetor squirted liquid fuel into the air intake in a fine spray, where it quickly evaporated and formed an explosive mixture with the air.

Other engineers tried to get more power out of an engine of a given size by running it on the two-stroke-cycle principle. That is to say, every downstroke of the piston is a power stroke. The exhaustion of the burned gases, the sucking in of a new charge of fuel and air, and the compression of the explosive mixture all take place during a single upstroke. Thus the two-stroke-cycle engine delivers twice as many power strokes as the Otto engine for a given number of revolutions of the crankshaft. In 1878, in Great Britain, Sir Dugald Clerk (1854–1932) constructed a workable two-stroke-cycle engine; Day built a better one in 1891.

Unfortunately, in a two-stroke-cycle engine, there is always some mixing of the burned gas that is about to be exhausted from the cylinder with the incoming charge of vaporized fuel and air. Either some of the burned gas stays in the cylinder during the power stroke, or some of the fresh charge is blown out the exhaust port with the burned gas. Since either process is wasteful, the two-stroke-cycle engine is less thrifty of fuel than the Otto engine. Two-stroke-cycle engines are used nowadays to power such machines as lawn mowers and outboard motorboats, where lightness is more important than economy of fuel.

The greatest triumph of the internal-combustion engine has been the automobile. The automobile, however, had to await the coming of several other inventions before it could become practical.

For example, automobiles need rubber tires. Rubber was known centuries before Columbus; the Indians of Central America played games with rubber balls. Pure rubber, however, gets brittle in cold weather and melts in hot. It did not become suitable for overshoes and tires until the 1830s, when an American inventor, Charles Goodyear (1800–60), discovered a method of combining sulfur with the boiling juice of the rubber tree. Although Goodyear's discovery was a great success, Goodyear, who had no business sense, died heavily in debt.

The automobile also got much of its inspiration from the bicycle. In 1799, a German, Baron Karl von Drais, brought out a bicycle called a "draisine." The draisine had no pedals; the rider made it go by striking his feet against the ground. Although it had a brief vogue in the 1820s, riders found it more strenuous than walking.

Throughout the nineteenth century, bicycle inventors tried out different arrangements of wheels and pedals. At last, in the 1870s, H. J. Lawson in England and William Pope in the United States combined the chain-and-sprocket drive with other older inventions to make the first bicycles of the modern type.

American roads at that time ranged from bad to awful. They were dust tracks in dry weather and rivers of mud in wet. The spread of the bicycle had much to do with persuading American lawmakers to build better roads, although the best of them were still of earth, occasionally topped with asphalt. The modern concrete roads and superhighway systems we are familiar with belong to the middle decades of the twentieth century, when antomobile traffic completely outgrew the older roads.

Engine-powered vehicles built to run on roads go back to the early days of steam. About 1770, even before Oliver Evans built his amphibious dredge, a Frenchman, Nicolas Joseph Cugnot (1725–1804), made two massive wooden steam wagons for towing cannon. These had an engine mounted out over a single front wheel. As these vehicles could go only two and a half miles an hour, had to stop every quarter-hour to get up steam, and could scarcely be steered, nothing came of the experiment.

Beginning in 1801, a number of inventors in Europe and

America experimented with steam carriages. In the 1820s and 30s, British steam carriages were improved to the point where a few enterprising Britons ran them as omnibuses on regular schedules. In 1838, Walter Hancock, one of the most active of these steam-carriage promoters, made a small steam carriage for his own use. This might be considered the world's first private automobile.

Soon, however, stagecoach owners, horse breeders, and other interested parties persuaded the British Parliament to pass laws that so restricted the steam coaches that their owners could not make a profit. The most drastic of these laws, in force from 1865 to 1896, required a man with a red flag to walk in front of the vehicle. Even without these laws, steam coaches might not have succeeded, because their engines were too heavy and bulky for the power they developed. Furthermore, the rough roads of the time soon shook their delicate machinery out of order.

What was needed was a small, light, but powerful engine with neither boiler nor furnace. The internal-combustion engine filled this need perfectly. In the 1860s and 70s, a number of patents were issued for vehicles powered by Lenoir engines, and some of these naphtha-burning carriages were built and run. Then, when engines of the compression type came in, experimentation became even livelier.

In 1879, when interest in the new engines was rising, a lawyer in Rochester, New York, George Baldwin Selden (1846–1922), applied for a patent on a "road locomotive" driven by "an engine of the compression type." However, instead of building an automobile, Selden built and tested a three-cylinder engine. This motor was an improved version of one invented by George B. Brayton of Boston in 1873. It is sometimes called the first two-stroke-cycle engine, although its principle differed from that of the modern two-stroke-cycle engine. The fuel-air mixture was compressed in a separate cylinder before being admitted to the power cylinder.

While tinkering with his engine, Selden set out to raise capital to build an automobile. Meanwhile he delayed the issuance of his patent, since there was no point in having his monopoly on automobiles start before there were any automobiles to collect royalties on. Selden, however, failed to get his money. Although a shrewd patent attorney, an able inventor, and a competent mechanic, Selden was no salesman. Impatient and irascible, he approached his prospective backers in such a forceful, dogmatic way that he usually put their backs up.

In the 1880s and 90s, a host of inventors in Europe and the United States built a swarm of vehicles. Some were powered by gasoline, some by steam, some by electricity, and some by clockwork that had to be wound up every three miles. The most successful inventors were the Germans Gottlieb Daimler, Nikolaus Krebs, and Karl Benz. Daimler (1834–1900), who had worked in the Otto factory, devised a light, fast gasoline engine, which combined the carburetor of Maybach (who became his partner) with the Otto principle. With this engine he built a pioneer auto and the world's first motorcycle.

Krebs and Benz worked for a firm of Parisian carriage makers, Panhard and Levassor. In 1894, this firm brought out an automobile with most of the modern features: a V-engine in front under a hood, a water-cooling system, a sliding-gear transmission and differential, brakes on the wheel hubs, and elliptical springs. Eventually Benz started his own company, which merged with Daimler's to form the still-famous Mercedes-Benz Company.

Early American experiments with automobiles, such as those of Elwood Haynes and Charles E. Duryea in the 1890s, had little effect on the history of the vehicle. However, some of the fashionable rich began importing French automobiles. Next, country doctors found that with an automobile they could visit as many patients in a day as they could see in a week with a buggy.

The idea of a cheap car for everybody was the inspiration of

Ransom E. Olds in 1899. Because Olds built his Oldsmobile factory in Detroit, this city became the automobile capital of the United States. For several years, Olds ruled the market with a small "runabout." Then he quarreled with his backer and left to form another company.

Olds's great idea, however, was taken up by a gaunt, thin-lipped tinkerer named Henry Ford (1863–1947). Although he was ignorant of everything outside the automobile business and was extremely crafty, ruthless, and hard-boiled in his business dealings, Ford was a man of extraordinary genius.

After fumbling for several years with expensive automobiles, Ford in 1906 brought out his Model T: a black boxlike vehicle, not pretty but light, cheap, and rugged. With minor changes, the Model T dominated the market for twenty years. Fifteen million were built. Ford and his executives led the world in the development of advanced methods of mass production. He paid his workers more than any other auto maker but nevertheless became one of the world's richest men.

For several years, Selden collected from American automobile makers royalties on his patent for a "road locomotive." Ford, however, refused to pay. When Selden and his associates sued, the courts declared that the Selden patent (which had almost expired anyway) dominated only automobiles with Brayton engines. As all automobiles were using Otto engines, the makers did not have to pay any more royalties.

Soon the automobile industry grew so large that it dominated much of the economic life of the United States. The auto-making industry became the leading customer of the steel, rubber, glass, and upholstery-fabric industries, which depended for their prosperity largely on the sale of cars. The finished automobiles became the main consumers of the products of the vast petroleum industry. Today the American people are the most highly motorized in the world, averaging one automobile to every three persons.

This enormous and ever-growing fleet of sixty million cars has brought grave problems to America. Automobile accidents kill more people each year than a small war. Traffic congestion gets steadily worse, despite the billions of dollars lavished on fancy highways. Public transportation withers away, because railroads and rapid-transit systems cannot carry passengers at a profit when so many people prefer to drive their own automobiles. The atmosphere of cities becomes polluted with harmful chemicals. But then, every advance in science or technology brings a host of new problems in its train.

Men talked for centuries of what fun it would be to fly. Some, from the eleventh century on, even tied wings to their bodies and jumped off roofs, breaking their legs or necks. The first successful human flights were made in balloons, invented in 1782 by the brothers Jacques and Joseph Montgolfier in France.

Balloons came into use during the nineteenth century for circus attractions, for exploring the upper air, and for military observation posts. During the American Civil War, a young German nobleman, Ferdinand, Count von Zeppelin (1838–1917), eagerly watched the operation of the Union's observation balloons.

During the last half of the century, several European inventors, mostly French, combined the balloon with power drive. In these craft, the gas bag had the shape of a football. Below it hung a car with airscrews turned by steam, electricity, gasoline, or muscle power. Powered balloons of this type came to be known as dirigible (that is, "steerable") balloons, or dirigibles, or airships.

The biggest dirigible balloons were those built according to the designs of Count Zeppelin. Returning from America an ardent balloon-fancier, Zeppelin served in two wars, retired from the German army, and began building airships of a new type.

In the 1880s, Charles Martin Hall (1863–1914), who founded the Aluminum Company of America, had developed a new electrical process for turning the mineral bauxite into the metal aluminum. As this light metal could now be had in quantity, Zeppelin built a series of cigar-shaped aircraft with rigid frames of aluminum girders. He covered the frame with balloon cloth and placed within a row of balloon-cloth cells filled with hydrogen gas.

In the First World War, the German Navy used these "zeppelins" to bomb Great Britain until most of these airships had been shot down. Because hydrogen is inflammable, a single hit from a shell, bomb, or rocket brought each vast structure to earth in roaring flames.

After the war, several nations—Great Britain, France, Germany, and the United States—experimented with rigid airships, both for military and for commercial use. They not only used German zeppelins left over from the war but also built new and larger airships. To avoid the risk of fire, most of these airships were filled with helium, which is found in American natural-gas wells, and which scientists like Robert A. Milliken learned to produce in quantities.

Because helium is denser than hydrogen, a helium-filled airship could carry only about three quarters of the payload of one lifted by hydrogen. Moreover, helium had to be bought from the United States. After the hydrogen-filled German airship *Hindenburg* blew up at Lakehurst, New Jersey, in 1937, the whole idea of dirigibles was given up. The design of airplanes had advanced to the point where there was no longer need for these huge, costly, fragile airships, which wafted through the sky like the ghosts of whales.

Although airplanes in the long run proved more useful than airships, the problems they presented were much harder to solve. Once up, an airship would stay aloft in spite of small mechanical difficulties, but not so an airplane. Air proved to be the most slippery and untrustworthy road that men have ever tried to travel. Men had to know how to fly a plane through the treacherous air in order to construct one that would work; but how could they learn to fly until they had an airplane?

During the nineteenth century, several British and French scientists worked out some of the laws of aerodynamics. They built model flying machines, which sometimes fluttered a few yards before crashing to the ground.

Samuel Pierpont Langley (1834–1906), the first person to make an effective study of the science of aeronautics, was a large, ruddy man, shy, dignified, and wholly wrapped up in his work. He began his career as an architect before he went into science as an assistant at the Harvard Observatory. For twenty years, he was Director of the Allegheny Observatory and a professor of physics and astronomy at the Western University of Pittsburgh.

At Pittsburgh, Langley's many accomplishments included a correct explanation of sunspots and the invention of a delicate instrument, the bolometer, for measuring the sun's radiation. In 1887, he went to work for the Smithsonian and the following year became secretary of the Institution.

At this time, Langley began an investigation of the properties of air. He built a whirling table with two thirty-foot arms, on the ends of which he mounted brass objects of various shapes to measure their lift and drag as an engine spun the table. He found that curved airfoils worked better than flat ones.

Then Langley built a series of model aircraft driven first by rubber bands and later by light little steam engines of his own design. He called them "aerodromes." In 1896, Aerodrome No. 6 flew nearly a mile over the Potomac River.

Langley was now ready to drop the project. But his friend Alexander Graham Bell, President McKinley, and the War Department all urged him to build a man-carrying flying machine. Langley let himself be persuaded.

Steam engines, Langley decided, weigh too much in proportion to their power. Therefore, he switched to gasoline engines. His brilliant assistant, Charles M. Manly (1876–1927), designed the first radial engine, with five cylinders arranged like the spokes of a wheel.

In 1903, Langley assembled his large aerodrome on the roof of a houseboat on the Potomac. With Manly at the controls, the aerodrome was launched. Alas! the flying machine fouled the launching device and crashed into the river.

Langley repaired his aircraft and two months later tried again. Again the machine caught in the catapult and crashed. This time it was totally wrecked, although Manly was unhurt.

Although Langley had come close to success, the newspapers savagely ridiculed him, and Congress forbade the Army to spend any more money on flying machines. Many years later, the aviation pioneer Glenn H. Curtiss (1878–1930) repaired Langley's aerodrome. With a number of minor changes, the machine made several short flights from a lake in New York State, thus proving how near Langley came to building a workable airplane.

Meanwhile, the brothers Wilbur and Orville Wright, who owned a bicycle shop in Dayton, Ohio, had been working on their own flying mahine. Although they had little formal education, they went about the project in a very intelligent, systematic way. They read everything on the subject, including Langley's Smithsonian reports.

Several men in Germany, England, and the United States had experimented with gliders—flying machines without engines. Some had been killed in pursuit of their hobby. Their main trouble, the Wrights decided, lay in the gliders' controls. Although sometimes fitted with rudders and elevators to steer them to right or left and up or down, gliders had no device for righting the craft once it started to tip over to one side.

This problem was solved by the gaunt, hawk-nosed Wilbur

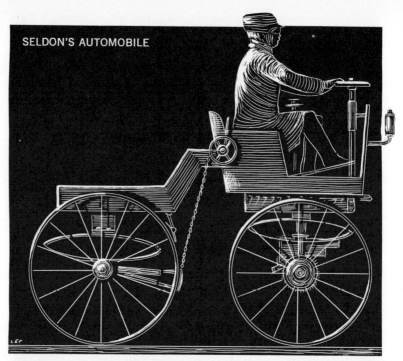

SELDON'S AUTOMOBILE

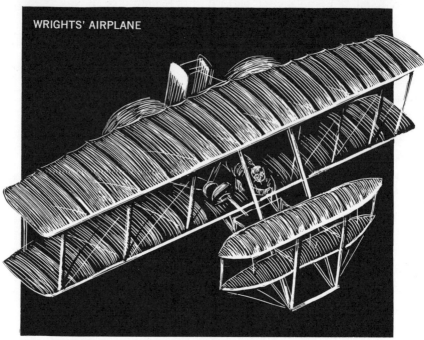

WRIGHTS' AIRPLANE

INVENTIONS OF THE INTERNAL-COMBUSTION REVOLUTION

Wright (1867–1912), the dominant one of the brothers. Wilbur Wright proposed to twist each wing as necessary by means of control cables, so that one wing could give more lift while the other furnished less.

For years they worked with kites, models, and gliders. Learning that Kitty Hawk, North Carolina, had strong, steady winds, they glided there until they had mastered the art of controlling their craft. Then they put an engine of their own design into one of their gliders. On December 17, 1903, nine days after Langley's second attempt at launching a plane, the Wrights made three short flights, the first a distance of 120 feet.

The newspapers, tired of stories of flightless flying machines, paid little heed. For several years, the Wrights flew near Dayton. One day they flew over a streetcar that ran near their field, causing a startled out-of-town visitor to cry:

"What's that?"

"Just one of them crazy boys," explained a local man. "Dern fools tryin' to make a machine that can fly. . . . You can't go agin nature." [1]

In 1908, however, the French and American governments both began to show interest in the Wrights' machines. By then, many other aviation pioneers were flying. The Wrights sued a number of these for infringing their patent. Although Wilbur Wright died in 1912 of a typhoid infection, Orville Wright (1871–1948) pressed the suits. The first of these was against Glenn Curtiss, the man who altered and flew Langley's aerodrome.

Curtiss was one of a group of aeronauts whom Alexander Graham Bell, a flying enthusiast in his old age, had financed. Curtiss thought he had gotten around the language of the Wright patent by equipping his airplanes with hinged flaps called *ailerons* at the wing tips, instead of warping the wings. The court, however, decided that the patent covered Curtiss's structures as well as that of the Wrights. So Curtiss had to pay Wright for infringing his patent.

A host of aeronauts in many nations built airplanes of many kinds in the years before the First World War. In 1909, the Frenchman Louis Bleriot (1872–1936) flew across the English Channel in the first airplane of more or less modern appearance, with the propeller and engine in front and the rudder and elevators mounted on an empennage at the end of a long tail.

Since then, airplane design has forged ahead. The two biggest advances were taken in Europe. The first was the all-metal monoplane with thick wings that needed no outside bracing, which was developed by the German engineer Hugo Junkers during the First World War and became the standard design for all the larger airplanes.

The other advance was the turbojet engine, developed in the 1930s by the Royal Air Force officer Frank Whittle. Instead of pistons moving back and forth in cylinders and turning a crankshaft by means of connecting rods, the turbojet engine has a blower and a turbine mounted on a single shaft. The blower, a many-bladed propeller inside a housing, sucks in air, which is mixed with kerosene and burned. The expanding gases from the combustion spin the turbine and roar out of a nozzle at the rear. The actual push, which moves the airplane, is exerted by the incoming air against the blades of the blower.

While the airplane was being perfected, many men also tried to make helicopters—machines that could fly straight up by means of airscrews on vertical shafts. Ideas for helicopters go back as far as Leonardo da Vinci (1452–1519), an Italian artist and engineer who lived at the time of Columbus and who left some beautiful drawings of such flying machines.

None of the early helicopters worked. For one thing, such a machine cannot carry so heavy a load in proportion to its power as can an airplane. Therefore, very light engines were needed. Even when these had been developed, helicopters proved unstable. After rising a few feet, they invariably tipped over and crashed.

The man who made the helicopter practical was a short, Russian-born American named Igor Igorovitch Sikorsky, the son of a professor of psychiatry. In Russia, Sikorsky experimented with helicopters. Before and during the First World War, he built the world's first four-motored airplane. He fled Russia at the time of the Revolution of 1917. Safely in the United States, he became successful as a builder of airplanes and then, in the late 1930s, devoted himself to the problem of the helicopter.

Sikorsky succeeded by means of an ingenious rotor-hub mechanism. This device causes the blades of the lifting rotor to change their angles of pitch as they go around the shaft. Thus Sikorsky allowed for the different speeds at which a blade meets the air in each revolution, as the helicopter moves through the air. In 1942, his company delivered its first helicopter to the Army Air Force. After the Second World War, helicopters of many types were put to civilian and military uses.

In the past century, the internal-combustion engine has conferred upon men a mobility far beyond that which the steamboat and the railroad gave them. It has made the magic carpet of the medieval Muslim storyteller an everyday reality; and it will go on whisking men around the world as long as the earth's supply of liquid fuels holds out.

XVI · THE DANGEROUS DEPTHS OF SPACE

The idea of voyaging beyond the ramparts of the world and visiting the heavenly bodies is an old one. In the fourth century B.C., the Greek playwright Aristophanes, in his comedy *The Birds,* told how two Athenian adventurers persuaded the birds to build an aerial city between heaven and earth in order to practice extortion on the gods. This might be considered the first vision of an earth satellite vehicle. Two hundred years later, a Syrian Greek, Lucian of Samosata, told of a flight to the moon by the crew of a ship caught up in a whirlwind.

Stories of journeys to the moon and other heavenly bodies continued to appear from time to time throughout the following centuries. The heroes of these stories reached their destination in a variety of ingenious ways. Some rode the prophet Elijah's chariot (Ludovico Ariosto); others chose a sedan chair powered by birds (Francis Godwin), or demons (the astronomer Johannes Kepler), or a monster cannon, Jules Verne), or an imaginary substance with negative gravity, repelled by the earth instead of attracted toward it (H. G. Wells), or just the motive power of a wish (Edgar Rice Burroughs).

The man who first suggested the one method that really works—the rocket—was a long-nosed French soldier and writer named Cyrano de Bergerac, who lived in the seventeenth century. As the twentieth century advanced, it became plain that Cyrano's idea was correct; that, if any man-made device could reach outer space, it would be a machine employing the rocket principle.

The rocket is an old device, invented by the Chinese in the thirteenth century. Soon thereafter, Arab scientists brought knowledge of rockets to Europe, where rockets were used for fireworks, for signaling, and sometimes for weapons.

The force that makes rockets go was first explained by Sir Isaac Newton, who stated his law that to every action there is an equal and opposite reaction. Some have thought that the stream of gas from a rocket pushes against the atmosphere, as a boatman pushes against the bottom of the stream with a pole. This is wrong. The gas pushes against the front of the combustion chamber, *inside* the rocket, whether or not there is any air outside. Thus a rocket works better in a vacuum, where there is nothing to stop it, than it could possibly work in the atmosphere. In fact, rocket propulsion is the only practical method known for driving a vehicle through airless space.

The mathematics of rocket flight were worked out by a deaf, modest Russian schoolmaster, Konstantin Eduardovich Tsiolkovskiy (1857–1935). In the early twentieth century, several scientists in Russia, Austria, Germany, France, Romania, and the United States developed Tsiolkovskiy's theories further.

One of these was the American Robert Hutchings Goddard (1882–1945), a slim, sharp-nosed man of retiring, secretive nature. In the First World War, Goddard served as an officer in the U. S. Naval Reserve, developing signal rockets. After the war, he built high-altitude rockets driven by a mixture of gasoline and liquid oxygen. One of these reached a height of 7,500 feet. Goddard cautiously proposed, in a Smithsonian report, to shoot at the moon a large rocket that should announce its arrival by a magnesium flare.

For twenty years, Goddard continued his experiments in New Mexico, published one more report, and kept aloof from other rocketeers. In the Second World War, he worked on rockets for the U. S. Navy but died of a throat infection just before victory was announced.

Between the two World Wars, such amateur groups as the American Rocket Society and the German Rocket Society experimented with rockets. They hoped to solve some of the problems of travel to other heavenly bodies.

In the Second World War, these experimenters went to work in earnest for their governments. All the leading nations involved in this war used rockets for military purposes. The most spectacular success was that of the Germans with their V-2, a 46-foot, fifteen-ton rocket powered by alcohol and liquid oxygen. With these V-2s, the Germans regularly bombarded London, two hundred miles away, leveling block after block of homes.

After the war, with the help of several former German rocketeers and the use of a number of captured V-2 rockets, the United States undertook large-scale rocket development. So did the Soviet Union. Both countries shot off their captured V-2s, one by one, while designing and building high-altitude rockets of their own. Since such rockets are very delicate and complicated mechanisms, there were many things that could go wrong with them; and in the early firings, many things did. Little by little, teams of scientists learned to manage their wingless horsepower and to control it from the ground.

A historic rocket firing took place at the White Sands Proving Ground in New Mexico, on February 24, 1949. The missile was not a single rocket, but a combination of two: a powerful German V-2 with a much smaller American rocket (with the unlikely name of WAC-Corporal) attached to its nose.

Goddard and other scientists had pointed out that a single rocket could not be expected to get very far into space. Most of its fuel would be used up just pushing its way into the upper atmosphere; and the weight of the empty tanks and the structure supporting them would slow down the missile once it reached the thinner air. The only possible hope for success lay in a two-stage, or two-step, rocket, with a very large rocket to start the combination skyward and a smaller rocket to ride the wild sky by itself once it reached the stratosphere. Some scientists suggested that an even smaller rocket might be carried in the nose of the high-riding rocket as a third stage or step.

The 1949 rocket shot proved the compound-rocket theory right. At a height of twenty miles, the smaller rocket cut loose from the larger one and went on to reach an altitude of 250 miles. At this altitude, the air is thinner than it is in the best vacuum made in a laboratory; therefore, one might say that outer space had been reached at last.

By this time, men's ideas about rocket engineering had changed greatly since the 1920s and 30s, when the heroes of countless science-fiction stories leaped into their rocket ships and took off for Mars or Neptune on a moment's notice. For one thing, the engineers learned that space rockets were so complicated and expensive that only the governments of the world's most powerful nations could afford to launch them.

Moreover, men have learned a great deal about the control of machinery by long-distance radio and have devised ways by which a machine can report back to earth its condition and the readings on its instruments. When, during the Second World War, remote control came into general use for testing experimental aircraft and for guiding missiles, the American armed services developed a variety of radio-controlled airplanes, bombs, and rockets. They also developed a system called "telemetering," by which an aircraft sends back to earth a continuous record of how its various parts are working during the flight. For instance, the test model of a new airplane has gages mounted on its various parts, to measure the stresses on these parts during its test flight. These measurements are continuously broadcast and are picked up and recorded by a receiving apparatus on the ground.

Finally, to furnish the instruments aboard such a rocket with power, a marvelous device was developed in the early 1950s at the Bell Telephone Laboratories. This was the silicon solar battery. The basic unit of this battery was a coin-sized disk of silicon, over the entire surface of which, except for one spot, had been placed a light coating of the element boron. When sunlight fell on the disk, an electromotive force of half a volt appeared between the spot and the rest of the disk. A battery of 432 such disks, mounted in a plastic frame, was first used to furnish power for a country telephone system in Georgia.

The silicon solar battery soon proved its value to satellite vehicles. When the early American vehicle Vanguard I was designed, the rockets available to American scientists were smaller and less powerful than those of the Russians. Because Vanguard I was no larger than a grapefruit and carried only 3.25 pounds of payload, it was equipped with the tiny silicon solar batteries.

Later, when more such satellite vehicles were lofted, the silicon solar battery became their usual source of power. These batteries enabled the vehicles to report their condition and that of the space through which they were traveling. Modern spacecraft often have large panels of silicon cells folded up so that the package fits into the nose of the smallest rocket stage. When the vehicle is on its own, the battery panels unfold, and the radio and radar antennae extend like the antennae of some colossal insect that has just crawled out of its cocoon to stretch its wings and legs for the first time.

Because the early American spacecraft could carry only small loads, their engineers developed to a high degree the art of "miniaturizing"—that is, making instruments and other electrical apparatus smaller and lighter than ever. The transistor, much smaller than the vacuum tube, was developed at about this time at the Bell Telephone Laboratories and made it possible to build miniature radio equipment. Later, when American space vehicles grew larger because of the invention of larger rockets to lift them, the value of these miniature instruments became apparent. American space ships could carry more instruments and consequently send back more information about conditions in space than could any competing country whose instruments were of a more average size.

In the year 1955, all the major nations of the civilized world decided to make a concerted attack on the unsolved mysteries of our earth and to share the scientific results of their researches. As a contribution to this International Geophysical Year, the American government announced that it would shoot into space a series of rockets carrying earth-satellite vehicles loaded with instruments to send back data on conditions outside the atmosphere.

After all this publicity, the American people received a shock when, on October 4, 1957, the Soviet Union launched into orbit the first successful satellite vehicle. This was the famous Sputnik[1] I, an instrument package 22.8 inches in diameter and weighing 184.3 pounds. It circled the globe once every 16.2 minutes, reaching an altitude of 560 miles above the surface and traveling about 17,000 miles per hour. On November 3rd of the same year, the Soviets launched a second Sputnik, in which was a capsule containing a dog, to see whether a mammal could live in space. They found that it could.

On January 31, 1958, the United States at last got into the space race with Explorer I, a slender cylinder 6 feet 8 inches long and 5 inches in diameter, weighing 30.8 pounds. Although not impressive compared to the earlier Russian satellite vehicles, Explorer I nevertheless made a first-class scientific discovery. When it climbed above 600 miles in its orbit, its radiation detecting device stopped working. Dr. James A. Van Allen of Iowa University correctly reasoned that the instrument was being jammed by more radiation than it could measure, and that the earth was encircled by one or more belts of strong radiation. Later satellite vehicles established that there were two of these "Van Allen belts" and mapped them.

During the years following these space shots, the governments of both the United States and of the Soviet Union spent vast sums on rocketry, each striving to be first in the space race. The Russians, having set the pace early, stayed ahead in most of the events: four months ahead in the first satellite vehicle orbited; two months ahead in the first shot into interplanetary space beyond the earth's gravity; ten months ahead in the first manned orbital flight; and so on.

The Americans, however, gradually closed the gap, while their more refined instruments collected great masses of valuable scientific information. Some people deplore this rivalry as a childish way for nations to behave. Childish or not, science has benefited from this competition, for it keeps the scientists of all nations on the alert. After all, Queen Isabella of Spain might never have backed Columbus in his search for a western route to the Indies if she had not heard that Portugal, Spain's great rival, was planning a similar expedition!

In the early stages of the exploration of space, it was a triumph to get any sort of satellite vehicle into orbit around the earth. Little Vanguard I, launched shortly after Explorer I, was the first such vehicle to take up a permanent orbit around the earth.

The orbit of any satellite around a heavenly body (as Kepler discovered 350 years ago) is an ellipse, with the larger body close to one focus of the ellipse. Because all satellites travel in ellipses, most of the early satellite vehicles launched by man passed close enough to the earth at their nearest approach to brush through the upper layers of the earth's atmosphere.

The friction of the atmosphere slowed them down, so that their next orbit was smaller, and the following orbit smaller still. In time, the vehicles spiraled down into the atmosphere and were burned up by the friction of the air they passed through. But Explorer I took an orbit well outside the earth's atmosphere. Several years later, it was still going strong; and this tiny man-made moon is expected to continue to circle the earth for centuries.

Other research satellites studied the Van Allen radiation belts, the earth's magnetic field; the "solar wind" of electrically charged particles that streams out in all directions from the sun; the number, size, and speed of meteoroids—those bits of cosmic dust and rock that fly about in deep space. They measured, more exactly than had ever been possible before, the pressure of the sun's radiation and the shape of the earth.

In addition to satellite vehicles intended purely for research, a number have been sent aloft for practical purposes. From 1960 to 1964, the United States put up eight satellites with the name of Tiros. These were drum-shaped vehicles equipped with television cameras and sending apparatus to take pictures of the earth and its cloud formations in order to keep track of the weather.

Over a hundred years ago, men realized that, to predict the weather in any one place, they required a continuous record of the weather over whole continents and oceans. With this information, storm formations could be detected and tracked on weather maps. Knowing how far away an approaching storm area was and how fast it was approaching, weather men could predict its time of arrival with fair probability. When Joseph Henry was Secretary of the Smithsonian Institution, he arranged for a regular exchange of weather reports by telegraph among a number of weather stations in the United States.

However, three quarters of the world is covered by water. Vast areas of ocean, lying outside of the heavily traveled ship and air lanes, roll and toss unseen by human beings able to report the weather. Hence, meteorologists could not obtain a clear picture of the weather over these immense stretches until the launching of the Tiros satellites. Now, these satellites send earthward a continuous televised motion picture showing hurricanes forming in tropical seas long before any weather stations on the surface of the earth could know about them.

Unfortunately, the Tiros satellites have one limitation: each of them was designed to point in one direction continuously with respect to the whole solar system. This means that, half

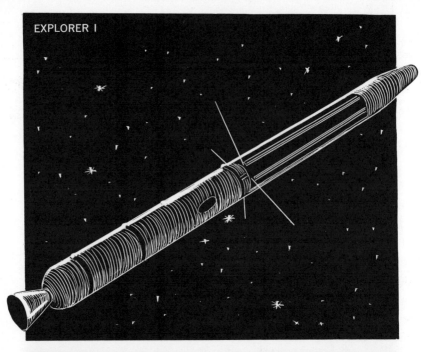

EXPLORER I

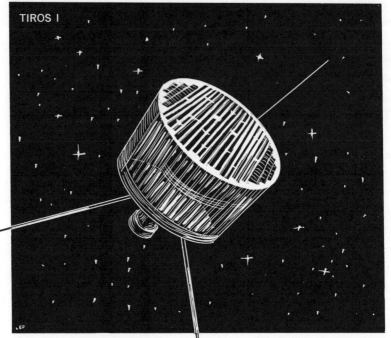

TIROS I

MODERN SPACECRAFT

the time, the camera in a Tiros is pointing toward the earth; while, for the other half, it is pointing away from it. Thus, Tiros can send good pictures of the earth's cloud cover during less than half its entire orbit.

Late in 1964, American scientists launched Nimbus A, the first of a new series of weather satellites designed to keep their cameras always pointing toward the earth. Whereas the Tiros satellites have orbits inclined to the earth's axis so that they scan only those parts of the earth lying between longitude 50° North and 50° South, Nimbus travels over the poles and therefore scans the entire earth in the course of a few orbits.

Another useful kind of space vehicle is the communications satellite, or comsat. In 1945, Arthur C. Clarke, a British writer and engineer, described such a satellite in detail in an article for a British magazine. Clarke suggested a number of features that were realized when such vehicles were actually built fifteen years later. With the rise of long-distance telephoning, the demand for voice communication between continents has increased so fast that cables and radio stations could not handle the demand. Moreover, telephone cables under the sea are costly, and transoceanic radio works only when the electrical conditions in the atmosphere are favorable.

Accordingly, a number of satellite vehicles have been launched into orbit for communication purposes. The first was Echo I, launched by the Space Agency on August 12, 1960. Echo I was simply a large balloon, 100 feet in diameter and coated with aluminum. It was shot into orbit in a collapsed condition, then inflated with compressed gas.

Echo I was a "passive-communication satellite"; that is, it simply reflected back to earth the radio waves shot at it. Since these waves were returned to earth on an angle, they could be picked up by receiving stations in places that could not be reached by a direct beam from the original sending station.

Because the reflected signals of Echo I were weak and required very powerful receiving apparatus, the next such vehicle was an "active-communication satellite," with receiving and sending apparatus by means of which the signal received could be amplified before it was returned to earth. Since this amplified signal is much stronger than that from a passive-communication satellite, and since it can be detected by a much smaller receiving apparatus, the extra cost of the active-communication satellite is more than offset by the saving in the receiving station.

The first active-communication satellite to go into orbit was Courier IB, launched October 4, 1960. (Courier IA had been destroyed when its rocket developed trouble during takeoff.) Courier IB worked for only eighteen days, but it proved that the theory was sound. A later American communications satellite, Telstar, although carried into orbit by a government-owned rocket, was the private property of the American Telephone and Telegraph Company. Telstar transmitted not only transatlantic telephone calls but also television programs.

Another series of American satellite vehicles, called Transit, has been adapted to the needs of navigation. These vehicles send out continuous signals by which ships can steer their course when clouds hide the heavens.

The most ambitious satellite vehicles to date have been those built to explore the other heavenly bodies and to carry men into outer space. Since instruments and radio-sending apparatus require much less coddling than a live human being, unmanned satellites, other things being equal, can be much lighter than manned satellites and thus can travel farther and faster with a rocket of a given size. On the other hand, a man in a space vehicle can make more varied observations than the most artful of machines. He can also make repairs and correct the machine's course more intelligently than can any remote-control device.

The first step in interplanetary travel was, naturally, to launch a rocket with a high enough velocity to escape the earth's pull and take up an independent orbit around the sun. Again the Russians were a little ahead of the Americans. On January 2, 1959, their "space probe" Mechtá ("Daydream") soared into orbit between the orbits of the Earth and of Mars. Two months later, on March 3, an American space probe, Pioneer IV, escaped from the earth's gravity and took up a similar orbit. On September 12 of the same year, another Russian vehicle, Lunik II, took off and thirty-five hours later struck the moon. On October 7, Lunik III (or Cosmic Rocket III as it is sometimes called) sent back to earth by radio the first photograph of the far side of the moon. (We earthlings never see this far side because the moon rotates as it travels around the earth and keeps the same face toward the earth at all times.)

Meanwhile, the Americans were working furiously on a series of moon rockets, called Ranger. Mechanical difficulties spoiled no less than six Ranger shots in succession. The last one, fired early in 1964, actually reached the moon—but the cameras failed to work. However, Rangers VII and IX, which made their journeys in 1964 and 1965, obtained excellent close-up pictures of the surface of the moon, which will be helpful when men actually try for a landing there.

Even more ambitious were the space probes launched toward other planets of the solar system. Once more, the Russians succeeded in being the first to get their vehicles into space. But now the bad luck that had caused the Americans so much grief in the Ranger launchings assailed the Russians for a change. The Russian probes to Venus and Mars both sped away on their proper courses; but in each case, the equipment aboard the vehicle failed, so that it could not send back the hoped-for records of its observations.

Starting a little later, the United States had better fortune. Mariner II, launched toward Venus on August 27, 1962, passed within approximately 20,000 miles of the planet on December 14th. Its instruments indicated that the surface of Venus— which cannot be seen because of the thick layers of cloud that cover the planet—had a temperature of about 800 degrees Fahrenheit. This is hot enough to melt lead; therefore, if the reading was correct, life on Venus is impossible.

Shortly after this, scientists at Johns Hopkins University in Baltimore sent a balloon with a radio-controlled telescope into the upper atmosphere. According to the observations of these research men, the surface of Venus might not, after all, be so hot as 800 degrees. No doubt, within the next few years, further observations will settle the question of the temperature of Venus and the possibility of life thereon.

An even more spectacular American triumph was the amazing work of Mariner IV, which headed for Mars on November 28, 1964. Six and a half months later, on July 14, 1965, the spacecraft came within 10,000 miles of Mars, took several photographs of the red planet, and transmitted them by radio over a distance of nearly 135 million miles back to earth. While these pictures failed to show the "canals" of Mars, they did show something quite unexpected: that the surface of this planet is pockmarked with many craters, like those of the moon, and probably caused in the same way—by the impact of large meteors or (as some astronomers think) by volcanic eruptions.

In the race to explore space by means of manned rockets, the Russians again jumped into the lead. Vostok I flew around the earth once on April 13, 1961, bearing Major Yuri A. Gagarin, the first man ever to travel into outer space. Vostok II, with Gherman Titov aboard, followed on August 6–7 of the same year, making seventeen and a half orbits around the world.

Meanwhile, the United States sent two astronauts on "suborbital" flights. They reached outer space only briefly and plunged back into the atmosphere without making a complete circuit of the earth. Colonel John H. Glenn made the first American orbital flight of three complete circuits, on February 20, 1962.

After that, both nations put more and more astronauts into orbit, each flight being an advance over the previous one. As this book was being written, two American officers, Gordon Cooper and Charles Conrad, spent eight days in orbit, traveling 3,300,000 miles and 120 times around the earth, and proving, before the splash-down on August 29, 1965, that man can live and work in space for the amount of time that it would take to journey to the moon and back. For the ultimate goal of present-day American and Russian space efforts is to land a man on the moon and bring him back alive.

Despite the enormous riskiness of the exploration of space, this work was carried on with a remarkably good safety record, until, early in 1967, the United States lost three astronauts, killed when fire broke out in their capsule during a ground test. A few weeks later the Soviet Union lost a Russian cosmonaut whose parachute failed to work on his descent back to earth.

Each year brings promise of future wonders beyond belief. The President of the United States has announced that in 1968 a Manned Orbiting Laboratory may be lofted into space, in which spacemen can work in regular business suits, in which they can stay a month or more, and from which they can descend to earth in a stripped-down Gemini rocket. From this orbiting cannister, men will make accurate maps of the continents, forecast weather, survey crop conditions, and study neighboring planets and radiations from the sun. They will also be able to detect nuclear blasts and missile firings, the better to defend our country against aggression.

As a result of the current interest in the conquest of space, the American aerospace industry receives over $20 billion a year of the government's money. It has become the largest industrial employer in our nation, surpassing even the vast automobile industry. The miracles of modern science are nowhere more evident than here, in the fulfilment of man's ancient dream to conquer space and to comprehend the mysteries of the great wild skies beyond.

XVII · SCIENTISTS OF TODAY AND TOMORROW

We have seen how American science started slowly and how, for over a hundred and fifty years, it lagged behind that of Europe. In the late nineteenth century, the United States at last took its place among the advanced nations of the world in applied science—that is, in engineering and invention. The results of this scientific growth have utterly changed the way of life of the American people, as one can readily see if he compares his life with the life in the days of Washington, or even of Abraham Lincoln.

Applied science, however, depends in the long run upon advances in pure science—studies of the natural laws on which our planet operates and of the way people and things react to them. If research in pure science were discontinued, applied science would languish, too, because new inventions, more effective medicines, and more efficient machines all depend on new scientific discoveries. Of course, to some extent, pure science cannot forge ahead without advances in applied science as well. Galileo could not see the moons of Jupiter until he devised an improved telescope; nor could more recent scientists study the structure of viruses without the electron microscope. Similarly, we learn more and more about the atmosphere and outer space as we create more refined rocket-powered space vehicles.

In the young United States, pure science grew much more slowly than applied science. By the end of the nineteenth century the United States had pushed into the lead in a few sciences, such as astronomy and paleontology, where climate and geography combined to make this land a splendid place for observation of the skies and the preservation of fossils.

After the First World War, pure science in the United States rapidly gained stature. The flight of leading scientists to America during the Nazi regime of the late 1930s gave American science a mighty boost. At this moment, the United States leads the world in science. Whereas, at the beginning of this century, there were only a few thousand scientists in all of our country, now there are nearly two million. A recent U. S. Government estimate indicates that there are about 1,700,000 scientists in America—500,000 pure scientists, 950,000 engineers and 250,000 high-school science teachers. This means that 2.8 per cent of the entire working force of the country is connected with science, as compared to 1 per cent in 1940.

The nation's working force of scientists has not only grown enormously in the last half century; it has also changed in makeup. There are fewer amateur scientists, since, as any science develops, it becomes too complicated and requires too much time and effort for amateurs to make useful contributions to it. Moreover, we find many more women scientists than formerly. In the middle of the last century, Maria Mitchell (1818–89), the daughter of a New England clockmaker, was considered a marvel because she became a qualified astronomer who discovered a comet and several nebulae. In 1865, she became the nation's first woman professor of astronomy and an ornament to Vassar College. Nowadays, nobody makes any special reference to the fact that a successful scientist is a woman, since women are found in practically all the sciences and have been particularly active in cancer research.

Although nobody knows for certain, the U. S. Government believes that, of the 1,700,000 scientists in America, 15.1 per cent are physical scientists; 7.4 per cent biological scientists; 6.7 per cent psychologists and other social scientists (a group that is rapidly growing); 56.1 per cent engineers; and 14.7 per cent science teachers. Of all our scientists, 57 per cent do industrial work, 11 per cent work for the government, 12 per cent are professors in colleges and universities, and 15 per cent teach in secondary schools. Five per cent have unusual or miscellaneous occupations, such as free-lance consulting on scientific matters.

Experts are uncertain about the exact number of scientists in the United States. They also disagree about the exact sums of money spent on scientific research. Yet, during the past ten or fifteen years, well over a billion dollars has been spent each year to promote scientific knowledge. Of this, about half has been spent by the Federal government and half by private agencies, including manufacturing companies, research groups, individual inventors, and nonprofit organizations like colleges and foundations. While the colleges and universities tend to specialize in pure science—studying abstract problems about the nature of man and the universe; the other organizations favor applied science—solving problems involved in making such better products as plastics, nylons, and weed killers. Even when research is carried on by universities or private companies, many do so only because they have contracts with the government. Thus, directly and indirectly, the U. S. Government supports about three-fifths of all the current scientific effort.

Today American science leads the world; but we have no assurance that this state of affairs will continue. For one thing, research in pure science is still handicapped by the old feeling, left over from our pioneer days, that pure science is unimportant because it does not give quick, profitable results.

For another thing, far too much of American scientific effort is going into engineering fancier automobiles, faster electric toasters, smaller vacuum cleaners, and the like. Better consumer products are all very well, as long as we remember that progress in applied science depends in the long run on research in pure science. Without new basic discoveries, engineering efforts sometimes result in useless fads.

Finally, the United States is running short of people trained in science. While the number of our scientists has multiplied many times over, the demand for scientific skills has been increasing even faster. At present, specializing in science is a sure guarantee of well-paid employment. Competition among companies for the services of young scientists has pushed their starting salaries from an average of $2,500 at the end of the Second World War to three times that figure today. Even college professors who specialize in science find themselves paid considerably more than the rather meager salaries of the professors of liberal arts.

Although starting salaries of scientific men are excellent, it must be admitted that the highest-paid jobs in American industry are those of executives in sales, advertising, and production departments. Rarely does a scientist or an engineer become president of the firm. Although now there is a small improvement in this direction, men from other departments usually pass him by on the promotion ladder.

Nor are all scientists equally fortunate in their careers. Those with specialties for which the demand is shrinking find themselves unemployed. Some find themselves in lines of work that may be labeled "research" but that actually involve dull, routine drudgery of little interest or importance. However, if a scientist picks an expanding line of work and is well-suited to his job, he is one of the luckiest of mortals. His work is also his play. He can spend all his working time doing what he most enjoys.

If scientific work is both stimulating and well-paid, why don't more young people become scientists? There seem to be several reasons. One reason is, of course, that only a minority of young people in any generation have the intellectual equipment. A scientist may succeed in spite of various shortcomings, but he must have exceptional intelligence. It is useless for a perfectly average mind, with an intelligence quotient of 100, to consider a scientific career.

Women scientists are fewer than men, not because they are less intelligent than men, but because in most cases they have to choose between a career and a family. Therefore, only exceptionally dedicated women become great scientists.

Moreover, a scientist must have a particular temperament. He must be curious, ingenious, bursting with ideas and, at the same time, skeptical and able to look at things in a cool, detached, objective way. People who have the intelligence to be good scientists but lack the temperament often do very well in other lines of work, like law, medicine, business, or the arts.

Doubtless, many young people who would make excellent scientists do not train for a scientific career. There are two problems to be overcome if we are to encourage enough new scientists to keep the United States in the lead and to improve the American standard of living.

The first problem is with our schools. Many public schools, especially in the country districts, offer few courses in science. Because of inadequate science teaching, many children with scientific aptitude never get a chance to develop it before they choose their working careers.

While most students, it seems, have been showing less and less interest in scientific education, the educational requirements for a scientific career have been getting steeper and steeper. A hundred years ago, men like Samuel P. Langley could become important and respected scientists without any special courses, merely by private study and on-the-job training. Nowadays, practically speaking, all scientists must have a college education; and in many branches of science they need a master's or a doctor's degree as well.

A MODERN COMPUTER

The only exception is in the field of invention, where a certain amount of useful work is still being done by amateurs and solitary individuals without special training. But, although the garret genius still exists and may survive for many years to come, he is becoming less important as more inventing is done by teams of highly trained specialists working in the laboratories of big universities or corporations.

The other problem America faces, in attracting more able young people into the various sciences, is to change the public image of a scientist. Ever since our pioneer days, when the best equipment for life was a handsome face, a stout heart, and a fast punch, people in the United States have rather despised the scholar. This attitude toward the scientific mind has been encouraged by movies, television shows, and comic strips. Here scientists are portrayed as figures of fun—vague peering duffers who know only words of four syllables and who are either foolish and impractical or downright sinister.

Actually, scientists are men much like other men. Some are conventional; others, eccentric. Some are conservative; others, radical. Some are shrewd; others, naïve. Some are modest; others, pompous. The only qualities they have in common are active, intelligent minds and a certain independence of thought, which tends to make them more individualistic and less conformist than the average person. To judge by their relative success in staying out of jail, the insane asylum, the divorce court, and the relief bureau, scientists tend to be quite successful human beings—certainly more so than the average man.

We have said that the United States now leads the world in science. But unless our nation encourages a new generation of scientists, it may soon find itself left behind. The Soviet Union has nearly as many scientists and engineers, right now, as the United States has and is training a new crop at twice our rate. The nations of western Europe, where education was disrupted by the Second World War, are also training about twice as many scientists per year as we are. Moreover, these nations are hard at work developing scientific leadership in many fields. Although scientific facts soon become known the world over these days, the country that first discovers them always outdistances the country that merely takes them at second hand. Nations have fallen before for less serious shortcomings than a lack of technical progress.

Many of those who are reading this book can carry forward the body of knowledge that has made our civilization the most amazing civilization the world has ever known. They should enjoy the challenge of searching for the still-hidden mysteries of the atom, of the human mind, of diseases, of wild life, of the ocean, of the skies. They can train for jobs in the world of tomorrow by learning all they can about the world today. And they can work for the peaceful application of the great discoveries of our times, so that they and their children after them may enjoy a longer, happier life.

NOTES

Chapter I, SCIENCE IN THE COLONIES
1. Mather, Essay xxvi.
2. Mather's diary for Nov. 14, 1721, quoted in Wendell, p. 279.
3. Letter from Franklin to Samuel Mather, May 12, 1784, quoted in Franklin (1945), p. 604, & Van Doren, pp. 43 f.

Chapter II, BENJAMIN FRANKLIN'S CENTURY
1. Letter from Franklin to Polly Stevenson, 1761, quoted in Van Doren, pp. 295 f.
2. Franklin (1945), p. 720.
3. Letter from Franklin to Collinson, 1750, quoted in Franklin (1945), p. 69.
4. Van Doren, p. 559.

Chapter IV, THE WORLD OF NATURE
1. Muschamp, p. 81.

Chapter V, EARLY INVENTORS AND INVENTIONS
1. Greek for "voice of the people."

Chapter VI, THE GREAT INDUSTRIAL REVOLUTION
1. McCormick, pp. 55 f.

Chapter VII, THE EXACT SCIENCES
1. Hylander, p. 24.
2. Moulton & Schifferes, p. 246.
3. Coulson, pp. 49 f.
4. Numbers xxiii, 23.
5. Rukeyser, p. 251.
6. Pupin, p. 288.

Chapter VIII, THE SKY ABOVE
1. Woodbury (1948), pp. 106 f.

Chapter IX, THE EARTH AND ITS WATERS
1. Maury, p. 25; Lewis, pp. 69 f.

Chapter X, THE REVOLUTION IN PHYSICS
1. Ralph E. Lapp: "The Einstein Letter That Started It All," in
New York Times Magazine, Aug. 2, 1964, p. 54. The preceding quotations are from this same article.

Chapter XI, THE SCIENCES OF LIFE
1. Osborn, p. 143.

Chapter XII, THE MOST MARVELOUS MACHINE
1. Jaffe (1944), p. 166.
2. Haggard, p. 258.
3. Pronounced "LAY-vun-hook."

Chapter XIII, THE SCIENCES OF MAN
1. Pronounced "AH-lesh HURD-litch-ka."
2. Pronounced "TOR-stun."

Chapter XIV, THE ELECTRICAL REVOLUTION
1. Coulson, p. 311; Mackenzie, p. 11.
2. Darrow, p. 285.
3. Coulson, p. 315; Woodbury (1944), p. 76. Thomson later became Lord Kelvin.
4. Bryan, p. 59; Josephson, p. 82.

Chapter XV, THE INTERNAL-COMBUSTION REVOLUTION
1. Goldstrom, p. 49.

Chapter XVI, THE DANGEROUS DEPTHS OF SPACE
1. Pronounced "SPOOT-nik," meaning "fellow-traveler."

SELECTED BIBLIOGRAPHY

ADAMS, FRANK DAWSON. *The Birth and Development of the Geological Sciences.* Baltimore: Williams & Wilkins, 1938; New York: Dover, 1954.

ANDREWS, ROY CHAPMAN. *Under a Lucky Star (A Lifetime of Adventure).* New York: Viking, 1943.

AKELEY, CARL E. *In Brightest Africa.* New York: Doubleday, Page, 1923.

ARCHER, GLEASON L. *History of Radio to 1926.* New York: American Historical Society, 1938.

ASIMOV, ISAAC. *Biographical Encyclopedia of Science and Technology.* New York: Doubleday, 1964.

BARBER, H. L. *The Story of the Automobile (Its History and Development from 1760–1917).* . . . . Chicago: Munson, 1917.

BARTRAM, WILLIAM. *The Travels of William Bartram.* New York: Macy-Masius, 1928.

BELL, ERIC TEMPLE. *Men of Mathematics.* New York: Simon & Schuster, 1937.

BOLTON, SARAH K. *Famous Men of Science.* New York: Crowell, 1926–46.

BOYD, THOMAS. *Poor John Fitch, Inventor of the Steamboat.* New York: Putnam, 1935.

BYRAN, GEORGE S. *Edison, the Man and His Work.* New York: Knopf, 1926.

BURLINGAME, ROGER. *Engines of Democracy.* New York: Scribner's, 1940.

————. *March of the Iron Men* (*A Social History of Union Through Invention*). New York: Scribner's, 1938.

CASSON, HERBERT N. *Cyrus Hall McCormick* (*His Life and Work*). Chicago: McClurg, 1909.

————. *The History of the Telephone*. Chicago: McClurg, 1910.

COHN, DAVID. *Combustion on Wheels* (*An Informal History of the Automobile Age*). Boston: Houghton Mifflin, 1944.

COPLEY, FRANK BARKLEY. *Frederick W. Taylor, Father of Scientific Management*. 2 vols. New York: Harper, 1923.

COULSON, THOMAS. *Joseph Henry, His Life and Work*. Princeton, N.J.: Princeton University Press, 1950.

DARRAH, WILLIAM CULP. *Powell of the Colorado*. Princeton, N.J.: Princeton University Press, 1951.

DE CAMP, L. Sprague. *The Heroic Age of American Invention*. New York: Doubleday, 1961.

DE FOREST, LEE: *Father of Radio, the Autobiography of Lee De Forest*. Chicago: Wilcox & Follett, 1950.

DORFMAN, JOSEPH. *Thorstein Veblen and His America*. New York: Viking, 1939.

EARNEST, ERNEST. *John and William Bartram, Botanists and Explorers, 1699–1777, 1739–1823*. Philadelphia: University of Pennsylvania Press, 1940.

FENTON, CARROLL LANE, and FENTON, MILDRED ADAMS. *Giants of Geology*. Garden City, N.Y.: Doubleday, 1952.

FESSENDEN, HELEN M. *Fessenden, Builder of Tomorrows*. New York: Coward-McCann, 1940.

FLEXNER, JAMES THOMAS. *Doctors on Horseback* (*Pioneers of American Medicine*). New York: Viking, 1937–44.

————. *Steamboats Come True* (*American Inventors in Action*). New York: Viking, 1944.

FORD, EDWARD. *David Rittenhouse, Astronomer-Patriot*. Philadelphia: University of Pennsylvania Press, 1946.

FRANKLIN, BENJAMIN. *Benjamin Franklin's Autobiographical Writings*. New York: Viking, 1945.

————. *Benjamin Franklin's Experiments* (*A New Edition of Franklin's Experiments and Observations on Electricity*). Cambridge, Mass.: Harvard University Press, 1941.

GOLDSTROM, JOHN. *A Narrative History of Aviation.* New York: Macmillan, 1930.

GREGORY, H. F. *Anything a Horse Can Do (The Story of the Helicopter).* New York: Reynal & Hitchcock, 1944.

HAGGARD, HOWARD W. *Devils, Drugs and Doctors.* New York: Harper, 1929; Pocket Books, 1959.

HAMMOND, JOHN WINTHROP. *Men and Volts (The Story of General Electric).* Philadelphia: Lippincott, 1941.

HENDERSON, DANIEL. *The Hidden Coasts (A Biography of Admiral Charles Wilkes).* New York: Sloane, 1953.

HERSKOVITS, MELVILLE J. *Franz Boas (The Science of Man in the Making).* New York: Scribner's, 1953.

HYLANDER, CLARENCE J. *American Scientists.* New York: Macmillan, 1939.

INFELD, LEOPOLD. *Albert Einstein (His Work and Its Influence on Our World).* New York: Scribner's, 1950.

JAFFE, BERNARD. *Men of Science in America.* New York: Simon & Schuster, 1944.

——. *Outposts of Science (A Journey to the Workshops of Our Leading Men of Research).* New York: Simon & Schuster, 1935.

JOSEPHSON, MATTHEW. *Edison.* New York: McGraw-Hill, 1959.

KAEMPFFERT, WALDEMAR (ed.). *A Popular History of American Invention.* 2 vols. New York: Scribner's, 1924.

KELLY, FRED C. *The Wright Brothers.* New York: Farrar, Straus & Young, 1943–50.

KUGELMASS, J. ALVIN. *J. Robert Oppenheimer and the Atomic Story.* New York: Messner, 1953.

LARSEN, EGON. *An American in Europe (The Life of Benjamin Thompson, Count Rumford).* New York: Philosophical Library, 1953.

LESSING, LEONARD. *Man of High Fidelity, Edwin Howard Armstrong.* Philadelphia: Lippincott, 1956.

LEWIS, CHARLES LEE. *Matthew Fontaine Maury, the Pathfinder of the Seas.* Annapolis, Md.: U. S. Naval Institute, 1927.

LEY, WILLY. *Rockets, Missiles, and Space Travel.* New York: Viking, 1944–57.

MABEE, CARLETON. *The American Leonardo* (*A Life of Samuel F. B. Morse*). New York: Knopf, 1944.

McCORMICK, CYRUS. *The Century of the Reaper*. Boston: Houghton Mifflin, 1931.

MACKENZIE, CATHERINE. *Alexander Graham Bell* (*The Man Who Conquered Space*). Boston: Houghton Mifflin, 1928.

MACLAREN, MALCOLM. *The Rise of the Electrical Industry During the Nineteenth Century*. Princeton, N.J.: Princeton University Press, 1943.

MADEIRA, PERCY C., Jr. *Men in Search of Man*. Philadelphia: University of Pennsylvania Press, 1964.

MARTIN, EDWIN T. *Thomas Jefferson, Scientist*. New York: Schuman, 1952.

MAURY, MATTHEW F. *The Physical Geography of the Sea*. New York: Harper, 1855.

MIRSKY, JEANNETTE, and NEVINS, ALLAN. *The World of Eli Whitney*. New York: Macmillan, 1952.

MORRIS, LLOYD. *William James, the Message of a Modern Mind*. New York: Scribner's, 1950.

MOULTON, FOREST RAY, and SCHIFFERES, JUSTUS J. *The Autobiography of Science*. Garden City, N.Y.: Doubleday, 1950.

MUSCHAMP, EDWARD A. *Audacious Audubon, the Story of a Great Pioneer, Naturalist and Man*. New York: Brentano, 1929.

NEVINS, ALLAN. *Frémont, Pathmaker of the West*. New York: Appleton-Century, 1939.

O'NEILL, JOHN J. *Prodigal Genius* (*The Life of Nikola Tesla*). New York: Washburn, 1944.

OSBORN, HENRY FAIRFIELD. *Impressions of Great Naturalists* (*Reminiscences of Darwin, Huxley, Balfour, Cope and Others*). New York: Scribner's, 1925.

PEATTIE, DONALD CULROSS. *Green Laurels, the Lives and Achievements of the Great Naturalists*. New York: Simon & Schuster, 1936.

PLATE, ROBERT. *The Dinosaur Hunters* (*Othniel C. Marsh and Edward D. Cope*). New York: McKay, 1964.

PUPIN, MICHAEL. *From Immigrant to Inventor*. New York: Scribner's, 1923.

RIESMAN, DAVID. *Thornstein Veblen: A Critical Interpretation*. New York: Scribner's, 1953.

ROBACK, A. A. *History of American Psychology*. New York: Library Publishers, 1952.

ROHAN, JACK. *Yankee Arms Maker (The Incredible Career of Samuel Colt)*. New York: Harper, 1935.

RUKEYSER, MURIEL. *Willard Gibbs*. Garden City, N.Y.: Doubleday, 1942–47.

SAUNDERS, JOHN RICHARD. *The World of Natural History (As Revealed in the American Museum of Natural History)*. New York: Sheridan House, 1952.

SCHUCHERT, CHARLES, and LeVENE, CLARA MAE. *O. C. Marsh, Pioneer in Paleontology*. New Haven: Yale University Press, 1940.

STERN, BERNHARD J. *Lewis Henry Morgan, Social Evolutionist*. Chicago: University of Chicago Press, 1931.

SUTCLIFFE, ALICE CRARY. *Robert Fulton and the Clermont*. New York: Century, 1909.

TURNBULL, ARCHIBALD DOUGLAS. *John Stevens, an American Record*. New York: American Society of Mechanical Engineers, 1928.

VAN DOREN, CARL. *Benjamin Franklin*. New York: Viking, 1938.

VON HAGEN, VICTOR WOLFGANG. *Maya Explorer (John Lloyd Stephens and the Lost Cities of Central America and Yucatán)*. Norman, Okla.: University of Oklahoma Press, 1948.

WENDELL, BARRETT. *Cotton Mather, the Puritan Priest*. Cambridge, Mass.: Harvard University Press, 1926.

WEST, GEOFFREY. *Charles Darwin, a Portrait*. New Haven: Yale University Press, 1938.

WHITE, RUTH. *Yankee from Sweden (The Dream and the Reality in the Days of John Ericsson)*. New York: Holt, 1960.

WILLIAMS, GREER. *Virus Hunters*. New York: Knopf, 1960.

WOODBURY, DAVID O. *Beloved Scientist (Elihu Thomson, a Guiding Spirit of the Electrical Age)*. New York: Whittlesey House, 1944.

———. *The Glass Giant of Palomar*. New York: Dodd, Mead, 1948.

INDEX

Adams, John, 22
aeronautics, 240
"aerodromes," 240
aerodynamics, 240
Agassiz, Alexander, 119
Agassiz, Jean Louis Rodolphe, 118
Agassiz, Louis, 154
ailerons, 243
air pump, 5, 16
Akeley, Carl E., 44–45
Alpha Centauri, 111
American Museum of Natural History, 41, 42
American Philosophical Society, 14, 21
amperage, 221
Amundsen, Roald, 24
Anderson, Carl D., 140
Anderson, Orvil A., 126
Andrews, Roy Chapman, 43
anesthesia, 173, 174
anthropology, 190 ff
antibiotics, 181–182
antiquarians, 197, 198
aqualung, 128
Arabia, 198
archaeology, 190 ff, 197 ff
Ariosto, Ludovico, 246
Aristophanes, 246
Aristotle, 130
Armstrong, Edwin H., 227
astronauts, 258–259
Astrophysical Journal, 103
astronomy, 105–116
atom, structure of, 135, 139, 140
atomic bomb, 146
atomic theory, 137
atom smashers, 142
Audubon, John James, 36–37, 38, 46
automation, 79, 82
automobiles, 79, 236 ff
Aztecs, 25

Baade, Walter, 113
Babbage, Charles, 80

Babylonians, 5
bacteria, 175, 176
balloons, 238
Banting, Frederick Grant, 180
Bardeen, John, 230
barium, 143, 144
Barnum, P. T., 44
Barton, Otis, 125–126
Bartram, John, 14, 15, 35
Bartram, William, 15, 35
Bass, George, 204
Bastian, Adolf, 193
bathyscaphe, 126
bathysphere, 126
Beaumont, William, 172
Becquerel, A. Henri, 121, 135, 136
Beebe, William, 125, 126
Bell, Alexander Graham, 215–216
Benz, Karl, 236
Bernier, François, 191
Bessel, Friedrich W., 110
Bessemer, Henry, 74
Best, Charles H., 180
Betelgeuse, 108
Bickmore, Albert Smith, 42
Binet, Alfred, 186
biochemistry, 180
Bleriot, Louis, 244
Blumenbach, Johann F., 192
Boaz, Franz, 195
Bohr, Niels, 136, 143, 144
botany, 14
Boucher de Perthes, Jacques, 193
Bouchon, Basile, 82
Bowditch, Nathaniel, 93
Boyle, Robert, 5, 6, 133
Boylston, Zabdiel, 9
Branly, Edouard, 225
Brattain, Walter H., 228
Brattle, Thomas, 7
Brayton, George B., 235
Breasted, James Harvey, 202
Broglie, Louis Victor de, 137
Brush, Charles F., 217
Bryan, William Jennings, 157, 159
Buffon, Comte de, 26, 27, 115, 121

DATE DUE			
Galloway SEP 7 '7|			
GAYLORD			PRINTED IN U.S.A.